Food

technology

LONGMAN

Addison Wesley Longman Limited
Edinburgh Gate, Harlow, Essex, CM20 2JE, England, and Associated Companies throughout the World

First published 1996
ISBN 0582 23466 2

Set in ITCKabel and Times
Designed and produced by Pentacor, High Wycombe, Bucks HP12 3DJ
Illustrations by Nathan Barlex, Oxford Illustrators, Pentacor
Picure researcher Louise Edgeworth
Copy editor Katie Chester
Indexer Richard Raper/Indexing Specialists
Printed in Great Britain by Scotprint Limited, Musselburgh, Scotland

The publisher's policy is to use paper manufactured from sustainable forests.

Project Directors
Executive Director Dr David Barlex
Co-directors Prof. Paul Black and Prof. Geoffrey Harrison
Deputy Director Dissemination David Wise

Contributors

Roy Ballam	David Barlex	Eileen Barlex
Michelle Bell	Ali Farrel	Judith Hallet
India Hart	Brenda Hellier	Debbie Howard
Margaret Jepson	Judith Powling	Mary Richmond
Ann Riggs	Marion Rutland	Anglea Sachs
Ian Steel	Jane Truscott	

We are grateful to the following for permission to reproduce photographs and other copyright material:

APV Baker 194; BBC Copyright centre 29; BCCCA 192, 193; Gareth Boden 44, 50 above, 51, 59, 72, 86, 105, 106, 119, 163 below right, 188, 199, 208; Chivers Hartley Preserves 198; Trevor Clifford 110, 174, 176, 177; Colorific! 90; Sue Cunningham 56; Department of Health 143; Mary Evans Picture Library 28, 32, 36 above; Fletcher Priest Architects 26, 27 (photo: Ian McKennell); Forte plc 189 above; Sally & Richard Greenhill 146; Robert Harding Picture Library 114 above; Health Education Authority 145; Intermediate Technology 56-57; Kellogg's 50 below; Longman Photographic Unit 31 below, 99; The London Planetarium 27 left; London Transport Museum 36 below, 37, 38; McDonald's Restaurants Ltd 165; Paul Mulcahy 189; Pictures Colour Library 190; Popperfoto 30; Powergen plc 25; Press Association/Martin Keene 31 above; Rex Features 112 left; The Royal Aeronautical Society 35; Science Photo Library 133, 147, 148, 149, 206; Mike Smith Photography 200; Stakis Hotels 189 below; Tony Stone Images 8, 9; Telegraph Colour Library 20, 40, 162; Unipath Ltd 33; Wellcome Trust 53.

The Nuffield Design and Technology Project gratefully acknowledges the support of the following commercial concerns in developing the published materials:

Intermediate Technology   Tony Sparkes at Chivers Hartley
Ray Ashbee at CABATEC   Irwin Desman Ltd
Covent garden Soup Company   Pret a Manger
Institute of Food Research, Norwich

Contents

Initial drawing   Finished plain muffin   Banana icing & cherry

Chocolate covered   Icing & 'hundreds & thousands'   Whipped cream & fruit

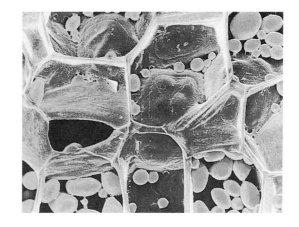

Contents

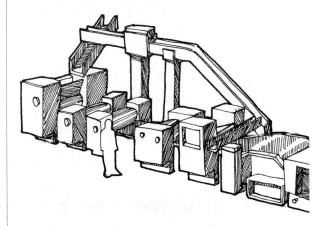

Part 1 Learning D&T at KS4

What will I design and make?

During key stage 3 you used a wide range of different materials for designing and making – textiles, food, wood, metal and plastic. At key stage 4 you are allowed to specialize in a materials area. You have chosen to specialize in designing and making with food. At key stage 4 you are expected to work to a higher standard in both designing and making; the quality of your products should be better than at key stage 3. The key stage 4 course lasts only two years and you simply don't have enough time to gain the extra skills, knowledge and understanding needed to improve your work in more than one material area. The sort of things that you will be designing and making are shown here:

▶ *Designing and making at key stage 4 is a real challenge. Your products should be good enough for the shops*

This area of designing and making is called **food technology**.

Of course there is more to design and technology than designing and making, and in your key stage 4 course you will also learn about the way design and technology works in the world outside school. In particular, you will study how industry is organized to manufacture goods.

I did these resource tasks:

SRT3   Design Briefs and Specifications
SRT5   Attribute analysis
SRT9   Evaluation by attribute analysis
CRT3   Developing that stand out factor
FCRT3   Foams
DFPRT2   Designing for flavour
DFPRT3   Designing for colour
FPRT1   Batch production

I read these case studies
Cold control – ice cream manufacture
Wrap it up
and the Design guide – from the confectioner

So I was able to design and make these ice-creams in a capability task

How will I learn?

If you do design and technology the Nuffield way then your teacher will use three different teaching methods. These are described below.

1 Resource Tasks

These are short practical activities. They make you think and help you learn the knowledge and skills you need to design and make really well.

2 Case Studies

These describe real examples of design and technology in the world outside school. By reading them you find out far more than you can through designing and making alone. Case Studies help you to learn about the way firms and businesses design and manufacture goods and how those goods are marketed and sold. You will also learn about the impact that products have on the people who use them and the places where they are made.

3 Capability Tasks

These involve designing and making a product that works. When you tackle a Capability Task, you use what you have learned through doing Resource Tasks and Case Studies. Capability Tasks take a lot longer than either Resource Tasks or Case Studies. Your teacher will organize your lessons so that you do the Resource Tasks and Case Studies you need for a Capability Task as part of the Capability Task. In this way your teacher makes sure that you can be successful in your designing and making.

Resource Tasks for gaining knowledge, skills and understanding

You will be given a Resource Task as an instruction sheet like the one below. All Resource Tasks are laid out in the same way. You will see that they are different from the ones you used at key stage 3.

code number   title

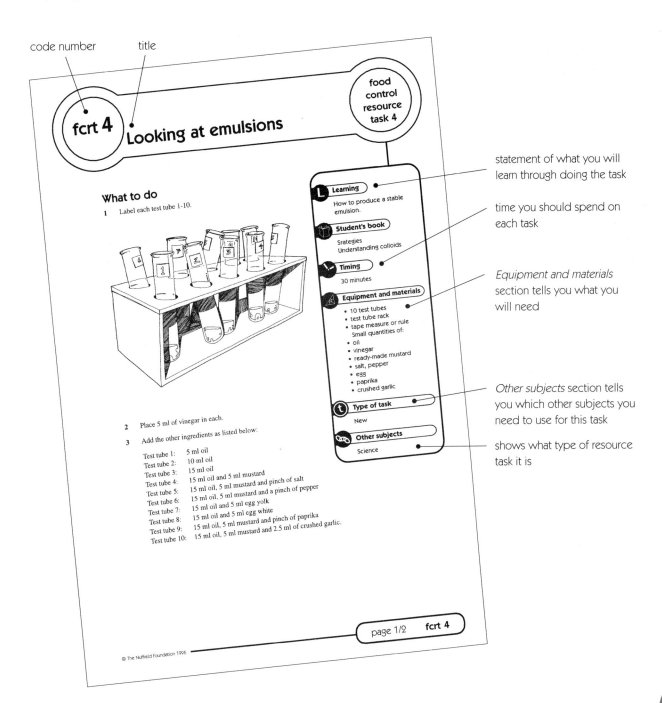

statement of what you will learn through doing the task

time you should spend on each task

Equipment and materials section tells you what you will need

Other subjects section tells you which other subjects you need to use for this task

shows what type of resource task it is

More about Resource Tasks

There are three types of Resource Task.

Recapitulation Resource Tasks

These are tasks that go over things that you probably did during key stage 3. They are very useful for reminding you of things you may have forgotten about or for catching up on things you have missed.

Extension Resource Tasks

These are tasks that take an idea that you were probably taught at key stage 3 and develop it further. They are useful for both revising key stage 3 ideas and helping you to use them in a more advanced way.

New ideas Resource Tasks

These are tasks that deal with knowledge and understanding that are new at key stage 4. It is unlikely that you will have done this sort of work at key stage 3. They are important for helping you to progress.

Your teacher may:

● organize the lesson so that everyone is doing the same Resource Task;

● set different students different tasks;

● allow you to choose from a range of Resource Tasks.

Sometimes you will work on your own and sometimes as part of a team.

Your teacher may introduce a sequence of Resource Tasks by talking to the whole class

Case Studies for awareness and insight

There are two types of Case Studies at key stage 4.

The first type are those that deal with 'large' technologies. These are the technologies which significantly affect the way people live. Often they are associated with a particular period in history. It is important that you read these Case Studies because they will help you to understand the way that technology affects our lives.

The second type are those that deal with products that are similar to those that you will be designing and making yourself. They describe:

- how the designs were developed, manufactured, marketed and sold;
- how the products work;
- how the products affect the people who make them, those who use them and others.

A particular Case Study may deal with just one of these or with all of them. It is important that you read these Case Studies because they will help you to design like a professional food product developer.

It is easy to lose concentration when you are reading a Case Study so they all contain questions which you should try and answer while you are reading them. It is often useful to discuss your answers with a friend. This will help you both to think about and make sense of the study. The Case Studies also contain Research Activities. You will often be set these for homework as they involve finding out information that is not in the Case Study.

A student presents her Case Study research findings to the whole class

This is important as it will help you to learn how to get new information as well as understand more about design and technology.

Capability Tasks for designing and making

Each of the products you design and make at key stage 4 will be from a group of product types. These groups of product types are called **lines of interest**. So, for example, you might design and make a product that was from the line of interest 'food products for those at risk'. Your product could range from a long-life, easy-to-cook, inexpensive meal for a student on a low income to a high-nutrition, easy-to-prepare dish for an earthquake victim. Certain sorts of knowledge, skills and understanding are useful for designing food products for those at risk, whatever sort of food it might be. These include an understanding of nutrition, the properties and qualities of food materials, preservation and packaging techniques – all these are needed to design and make an appropriate product.

We have suggested seven lines of interest for Capability Tasks in the area of food technology. Some possible products from each line of interest are shown opposite.

During your key stage 4 course you will have the opportunity to work in at least three different lines of interest. If you were to work in only one line of interest, while you would end up knowing a lot about that particular part of design and technology there would be other parts you would know nothing about at all. If you were to work in many more than three lines of interest you wouldn't have the time to study anything in depth so you would end up knowing very little about any part of design and technology. Working in three lines of interest will enable you to gain a reasonable level and range of knowledge, understanding and skill in design and technology.

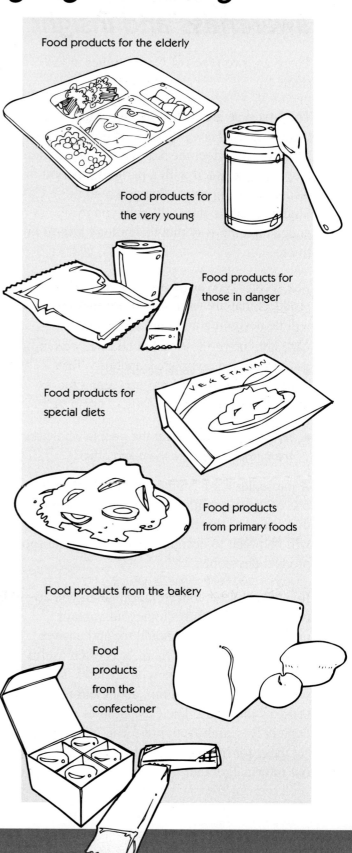

Food products for the elderly

Food products for the very young

Food products for those in danger

Food products for special diets

Food products from primary foods

Food products from the bakery

Food products from the confectioner

How many Capability Tasks?

If you are doing a full GCSE course it is likely that you will tackle three Capability Tasks during year 10, each one from a different line of interest. Your teacher will work out with you which ones your class will tackle. In year 11 you can either revisit a line of interest or tackle a new one. The one in year 11 will probably be your GCSE coursework. This makes sense because you should be better at designing and making in year 11 than you are in year 10.

It will be quite a struggle to fit three complete Capability Tasks into year 10 so your teacher may organize the lessons so that you only do part of some of these tasks. You will certainly need to do one complete Capability Task where you design and refine a food product through several stages of development before making and testing the well-finished product. In another Capability Task you might only produce a first prototype and leave out any refining to develop improved versions. This

means you will need less time. In another Capability Task you might only produce a series of design proposals as recipe suggestions. This cuts down the time you spend on the Capability Task even further.

Your teacher may give the class a design brief plus a specification and ask you to design and make a product that meets those requirements. Your teacher might even give you the brief, the specification and the recipe and ask you to make the product so that you can learn about the manufacturing process. Of course it is important that you carry out the Resource Tasks and Case Studies needed for each of these Capability Tasks. In this way you acquire a lot of design and technology knowledge, understanding and skills and still keep in touch with designing and making. This will put you in a strong position to tackle a full Capability Task in year 11.

If you are taking a short GCSE course in food you will probably tackle two shortened and one full Capability Task.

◗ A Capability Task can be work stopped at different stages

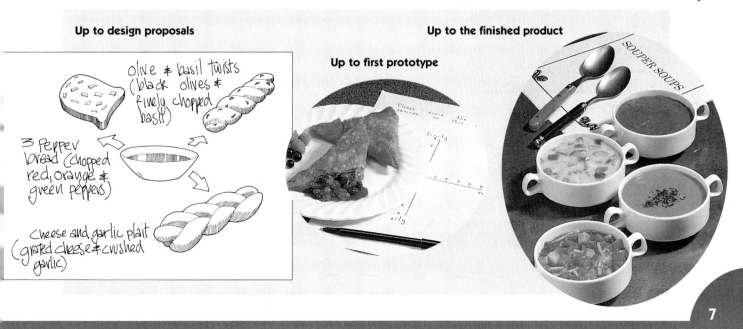

Up to design proposals

olive & basil twists (black olives & finely chopped basil)

3 pepper bread (chopped red, orange & green peppers)

cheese and garlic plait (grated cheese & crushed garlic)

Up to first prototype

Up to the finished product

SOUPER SOUPS

Ensuring your designing makes sense

You will be working to a brief which summarizes the following information about your product:

- what it will be used for;
- who will use it;
- where it might be used and where it might be sold.

This will help you to think about the design of your product. It will also help you to write the specification. You will need to use the brief and the specification as references for your designing. By checking your design ideas against the brief and specification you will be able to see whether they are developing in sensible directions.

This checking is often called **reviewing** and it is very important. If you fail to review your work at the correct times you will almost certainly waste a lot of time and your design ideas are likely to be inappropriate and in some cases may not work at all.

First stage review

Once you have some ideas for your product in the form of a written description plus some quickly drawn annotated sketches, you can begin your first review by comparing your ideas with the requirements of the brief and the specification. Ask yourself the following questions for each design idea.

- Will the design do what it is supposed to?
- Will the design be suitable for the users?
- Will the design fit in with where it might be used or sold?
- Does the design look right for the users and sellers?
- Have I noted any special requirements the design will need to meet later on?

Any design ideas that do not get a 'yes' to all these questions should be rejected or adjusted. In this way you can use the first review to screen out any design ideas that do not meet your requirements. You can do this screening in two ways:

- on your own, just thinking it through in your head and making notes against each design idea;
- working in pairs or a group explaining your ideas to other students in your group who can check them out against the questions. This takes longer and you have to help the others in the group check out their design ideas as well. But the extra time is usually well spent as other people are often more objective in their criticism of your ideas than you are.

Which ever way you choose, it will be important to discuss your review findings with your teacher.

Second stage reviews

By screening your early ideas you will be able to focus your efforts on developing a completed food product. It is important to produce a first prototype quickly so that you can test it and modify it in a series of second stage reviews. You will record these modifications as a mixture of annotated sketches describing the effects of changes in cooking methods, ingredients, freezing and thawing; the results of tasting sessions; photographs; sometimes rendered presentation drawings; and the instructions for making (recipes). To make sure that you develop your product in a sensible direction you will need to ask the following questions as you test and modify.

- Does it meet the flavour and texture requirements?
- Is the appearance (shape, size, colour) suitable?
- Does it meet nutritional requirements?
- Can I purchase the ingredients within the agreed budget?
- Will it have the required storage characteristics?

Once you are satisfied that your product will meet the requirements of the specification you can produce a final version. You will need to be clear about the time available for this final making and ask yourself the following questions.

- Will the ingredients I need be available when I need them?
- Will the tools and equipment be available when I need them?
- Am I sure that I can get the final appearance that I need?
- Have I got enough time for finishing and presenting my food product?
- Is there anything I can do to make my making more efficient?

You are probably the only one who can answer these questions but it will be worth checking your answers with your teachers as they are likely to know about any hidden traps and pitfalls.

Evaluating the final products

Here are examples of the ways in which you can evaluate your design once you have made it. You can find out more about them in the *Strategies* section (pages 92–97). It will be important to use all these different methods in coming to a judgement about the quality of your design.

User trip

By interviewing the user, Noreen was able to find out what she did and didn't like about the inexpensive food products she had developed.

Performance specification

Gupta designed a series of low-calorie dishes entitled 'Weight watching around the world'. The specification was as follows.

- Each dish to be less than 250 calories.
- Each dish to be cooked either conventionally or with a microwave.
- Each dish to be based on a recipe from a different country.

He was surprised to find that only some of the dishes were successful in the microwave. It is important to design your product to meet all the specification requirements.

Winners and losers

Jane designed a range of healthy snacks for children at the local playgroup. They replaced the jam tarts that the pensioners' club made. Jane's snacks were much healthier than the jam tarts – low in sugar and fat, containing fresh vegetables – so it seemed at first that everyone would gain if her design was used. But what about the feelings of the pensioners? What about the raffle they organize to support the playgroup – would this still go ahead? What about the children who like jam tarts? By thinking about winners and losers Jane could see that it was quite complicated.

Appropriateness

Fred designed a series of confectionery novelties to be sold as small gifts. He had designed them to be made by simple hand-operated machines with hand finishing and packing so that their production would provide work in a depressed area as part of a regeneration scheme. By asking the questions on page 97 he was able to decide whether his design was appropriate.

Thinking about how well your product meets its specification

One way to do this is to discuss your product with some other students. Give your product a blob score for each part of the specification – 5 blobs if it meets that part really well, 3 blobs if it meets it moderately well, 1 blob if it meets it only poorly and no blobs if it fails to meet this part of the specification. The next part is the tricky bit. Explain to the other students in the group why you have given the scores you have. Their job is to question your judgements. Your job is to convince them that your judgements are correct. If you do this you will be in a good position to move on to looking at your progress.

Looking at your own progress

At the end of a Capability Task it is important to look back at what you have done and reflect on your progress. The following sets of questions will help you with this.

Feeling good about what you have done

- Am I proud of what I made?
- Can I explain why?
- Am I proud of the design I developed?
- Can I explain why?

Understanding the problems

- What sorts of things slowed me down?
- Can I now see how to overcome these difficulties?
- What sorts of things made me nervous so that I didn't do as well as I know I could?
- Do I know where to get help now?
- What sorts of things did I do better than I expected?
- Was this due to luck or can I say that I'm getting better?
- Were there times when I concentrated on detail before I had the broad picture?
- Were there times when I didn't bother enough with detail?

- Can I now see how to get the level of detail right?

Understanding yourself

- Were there times when I lost interest?
- Can I now see how to get myself motivated?
- Were there times when I couldn't work out what to do next?
- Can I now see how to get better at making decisions?
- Were there times when I lost my sense of direction?
- Can I now see how to avoid this?

Understanding your design decisions

- With hindsight can I see where I made the right decisions?
- With hindsight can I see where I should have made different decisions?
- With hindsight can I see situations where I did the right thing?
- With hindsight can I see where I would do things differently if I did this again?

1

Part 2
Using other subjects in D&T at KS4
Using science

At key stage 4 you will be able to use science when you are tackling Capability Tasks. This is different from using science in a Resource Task. In a Resource Task you will be **told** to use science in the, 'other subjects' section. In a Capability Task you have to **choose** when to use science.

Your science lessons will teach you two main things. First, how to carry out scientific investigations. If you need to find something out in a Capability Task, say the best temperature for stir-frying or which ingredients in a recipe are responsible for stabilizing a salad dressing emulsion, then you can use your science to help you plan the investigation and design the necessary experiments. Second, in science you will acquire scientific knowledge which could be useful in understanding the nature of food and eating. This is given in the panel below. Note that some of the science is from key stages 2 and 3 as well as key stage 4.

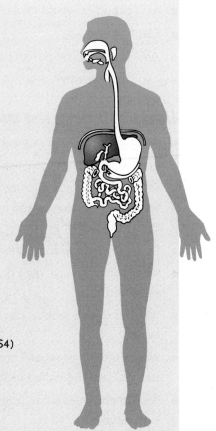

Science that is important for food product design

Life processes and living things

Humans as organisms

Teeth and dental care (KS2)

The importance of a varied and adequate diet (KS2)

The components of a balanced diet (KS3)

The sources of the main food components (KS3)

The effects of harmful substances (KS2, KS3 and KS4)

Human digestion (KS3 and KS4)

Living things in the environment

Food chains and the effects of toxic materials (KS2, KS3 and KS4)

Understanding micro-organisms (KS2 and KS4)

Food production for efficient energy transfer (KS4)

Materials and their properties

Bonding

Understanding molecular, polymeric and giant structures of food (KS4)

Patterns of behaviour

Acidity and alkalinity (KS3)

Enzymes in the food industry (KS4)

Using mathematics

At key stage 4 you will need to use your understanding of mathematics to help your design and technology. You will be able to use mathematics when you are tackling Capability Tasks. This is different from using mathematics in a Resource Task. In a Resource Task you will be **told** to use mathematics in the 'other subjects' section. In a Capability Task you have to **choose** when to use mathematics. Often you use mathematics without realizing it. The panel below shows some examples.

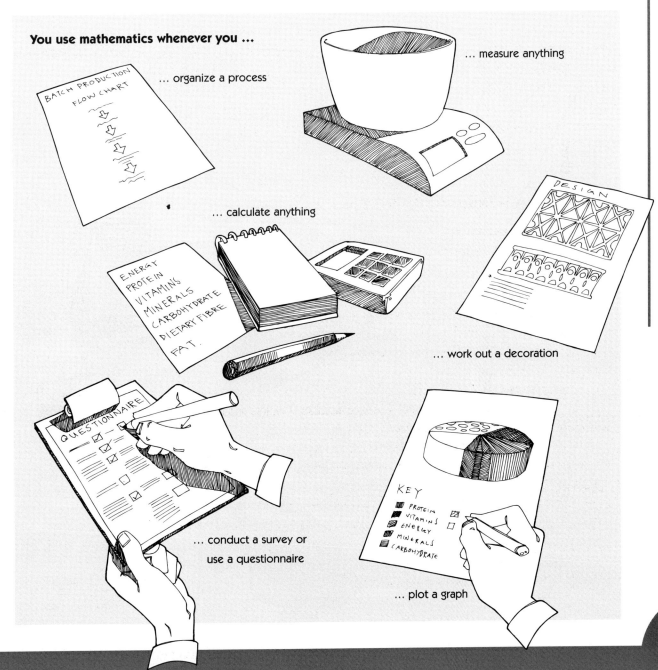

You use mathematics whenever you ...

... organize a process

BATCH PRODUCTION FLOW CHART

... measure anything

... calculate anything

ENERGY
PROTEIN
VITAMINS
MINERALS
CARBOHYDRATE
DIETARY FIBRE
FAT

DESIGN

... work out a decoration

QUESTIONNAIRE

... conduct a survey or use a questionnaire

KEY
PROTEIN
VITAMINS
ENERGY
MINERALS
CARBOHYDRATE

... plot a graph

Using art

At key stage 4 you will need to use your understanding of art to help your design and technology. You will be able to use art when you are tackling Capability Tasks. This is different from using art in a Resource Task. In a Resource Task you will be **told** to use art in the 'other subject' section. In a Capability Task you have to **choose** when to use art. The example below shows how one student has used art in developing the design of confectionery based on animals.

Children's Food Purchase Survey

Instructions to interviewer.

Write '1' in the box by each answer given, except where the printed instructions tell you to do something else.

1   Have you just bought any food products for a child?
    ☐ 1 *Yes*   0 *No* (If No, terminate the interview)

2   How old is the child for whom the food was bought?
    ☐ *Write whole number of years*

3   Is the child a girl or a boy? or
    ☐ Are you a girl or a boy?

4   Which one of the following categories best describes the food?
    ☐ A Breakfast cereal   B Cake   C Sweets
       D Biscuit   E Crisps F Yoghurt

5   When is the food product likely to be eaten?
    ☐ A Breakfast   B Lunch   C Tea
       D Dinner   E Between meals

6   How much did you pay?
    ☐ *Write the amount in pounds and pence like this:1.50*

7   Had you decided what you would buy before you entered the shop, or did you look first and then decide?
    ☐ *Write 1 for 'decided before',*
       2 for 'decided after'

8   Was your decision based on what food was like or how much it cost?
    ☐ *Write 1 for 'What food was like',*
       2 for 'How much it cost'

Using information technology

At key stage 4 you will need to use your understanding of information technology to help your design and technology. You will be able to use information technology when you are tackling Capability Tasks. This is different from using information technology in a Resource Task. In a Resource Task you will be **told** to use information technology in the 'other subjects' section. In a Capability Task you have to **choose** when to use information technology. The examples here show how students used information technology to find out about the sales of existing products and to use nutritional information.

◨ *Questionnaire on food purchase designed for use with a database*

◨ *Rapid nutritional analysis made possible by computer*

Part 3
How you will be assessed at GCSE

Writing your own Capability Task

If you are taking a full GCSE course it is likely that the Capability Task you tackle in year 11 will be the one that will be used for your GCSE coursework. This makes sense because you should be better at designing and making in year 11 than you are in year 10. Here are some guidelines to help you.

Designing the Capability Task

1 Deciding on the line of interest

Answer these questions in your design folder.

- Do you want to revisit a line of interest from year 10, or do you want to try something new?
- Which Resource Tasks did you enjoy most? Are these linked to a line of interest?
- Is there a group of students in your class that want to work on a particular line of interest?

2 Justifying your decision

Answer these questions in your design folder.

- Who will benefit from the product I am going to design and make?
- Will I be successful at designing and making this sort of product?
- Can I afford to make this sort of product?

3 Sorting out any extra learning that might be necessary

It is not difficult to identify particular aspects of design and technology knowledge that are likely to be useful for your task. Discuss this with your teacher and list Resource Tasks that could be useful in your design folder.

4 Identifying any Case Studies that might provide useful background reading

Read and make notes in your design folder listing those points that are relevant to your task.

5 Drawing up a 'Using other subjects' checklist

Discuss this with your D&T teacher.
Check with your other subject teachers if you think they can help.

6 Working with other people

There may be parts of your Capability Task that could benefit from a team approach – carrying out a survey, collecting reference materials, brainstorming ideas, for example. You will need to organize these joint ventures carefully so that everybody's task is improved.

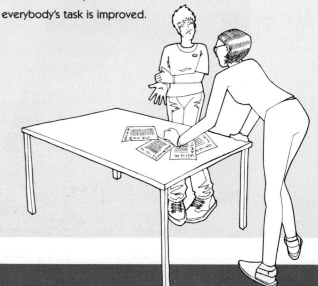

Tackling the Capability Task

7 Writing a design brief and developing a specification

You must remember that you are expected to design and make a quality product that meets demanding criteria. These should take into account not only taste, nutrition, appearance and cost but also how it could be manufactured, how it should be stored once purchased, how it can be safely prepared and how it might be sold.

8 Generating design ideas

You will need to show where your ideas come from. Make sure you keep a record of your early thoughts.

9 Developing your ideas

You will need to keep a clear record of the first prototype product you made, and the tests you carried out in order to refine it.

10 Photographs, presentation drawings and recipes

These should show what your design will look like and how it can be made.

11 Developing quality assurance production

12 Making your product

13 Evaluating the final product

Make sure you use a range of techniques.

14 Putting on a display

You should mount a display that shows your work to best advantage. It should describe the following:

- your ideas and where they came from;
- how they developed;
- photographs, presentation drawings and recipes;
- your schedule for quality assured production;
- your evaluation.

Writing your own Case Study

You may have to write your own Case Study as part of your GCSE assessment. Here are some guidelines.

Which product?

You should choose an everyday item that is manufactured. You should be able to examine it, use it yourself, see others use it and evaluate it. Here are some possibilities:

- a breakfast cereal;
- a sweet snack bar such as a KitKat or Mars Bar;
- a savoury snack such as crisps or munchies;
- a quick-cook snack such as Pop Tarts or Pot Noodles;
- a ready-to-cook meal such as a pasta or curry dish;
- a ready-to-eat or easy-to-cook dessert;
- a soft drink such as Tango or Iron Bru.

What should it describe?

Your study should describe the following:

- what the product looks like;
- what the product tastes like;
- what nutritional requirements the product meets;
- what part it is likely to play in a person's diet;
- who uses the product and what they think of it;
- how it's made;
- how much the product costs to buy;
- how this compares with the money likely to be spent on a day's food;
- the marketing and advertising used;
- the impact the product has made on the way people live.

You may compare several similar products if you think this will give interesting findings.

How many words?

No more than about 2000 words. (One side of A4 paper filled with typing is about 500 words.)

What about pictures?

It is important to use illustrations as well as text. You can use any of the following:

- your own illustrations drawn directly onto the page or pasted in place;
- illustrations photocopied from books or magazines and pasted in place;
- your own illustrations scanned onto disc and printed in place;
- illustrations taken from a library on CD ROM and printed in place.

What about layout?

If possible use desk-top publishing (DTP) software to produce your Case Study. If this is not available use word-processing (WP) software to lay out the text. If this is not available use a typewriter.

What about the overall length?

A reasonable mixture of text and pictures will give you a length of about 12 sides of A4.

What about special features?

You can make your Case Study:

- *attractive* by producing an illustrated cover;
- *easy to look through* by numbering the pages, using headings and producing a title page and contents page;
- *easy to understand* by using illustrations with notes and captions.

Examination questions

You may have to take a final written examination paper at the end of year 11 as part of your GCSE assessment. This paper will be made up of different sorts of questions. Here is a guide to some of these questions and how to answer them.

Interpreting a short Case Study

In this sort of question you will be given two or three paragraphs to read and one or two pictures to look at. The writing and the pictures will describe an aspect of design and technology from the real world. You will then have to answer a series of questions based mainly on what you have read. Some will involve finding a piece of information from the text. If you read the text carefully you can always get these questions right. Some will involve explaining something that is described in the text. These are more difficult as they will require you to use your design and technology knowledge and understanding. Some will ask you to make a judgement about the effects of the design and technology described. These are the most difficult but if you think carefully you will be able to use your design and technology awareness and insight to make judgements and give good reasons to back them up.

Presenting and interpreting information

In this sort of question you will be given data from some design and technology research and asked to present it in a way that makes it easy to understand. The data comes from very different sources. It could be about consumer preferences, the results of testing a production schedule, production figures for different manufacturing methods or sales figures for different products. Once you have presented the data you will be asked questions that require you to interpret the data.

Why is it like that?

In this sort of question you will be given information about a product in the form of annotated illustrations and text. You will be asked to explain different features of the design such as:

- why particular ingredients have been chosen;
- why the product looks the way it does;
- what nutritional requirements are met by the product;
- what would happen if certain things were changed;
- how the product might be manufactured;
- how the design might be improved;
- to what market the product is likely to appeal.

You will have to use the design and technology knowledge and understanding you have learned throughout years 10 and 11 to give correct answers.

What could you use for that?

In this sort of question you will be given a short technical design problem. You will be presented with an incomplete design to which there are several different possible solutions. Your task will be in three parts:

1 to describe some of the possible solutions by means of simple annotated sketches;

2 to compare these solutions;

3 to state clearly which solution you think is the best with reasons.

Again you will have to use the design and technology knowledge and understanding you have learned throughout years 10 and 11 to give correct answers.

Questions 1 and 2 are taken from the Welsh Joint Education Committee GCSE Specimen Paper. They deal with food safety and quality control during food production; packaging and product information.

1 Manufacturers take considerable care with food production systems to ensure products are safe to eat and of consistent quality.
   Suggest **two** steps in the production planning of a pizza to ensure:

   (a) the micro biological safe production of the pizza   *(4 marks)*

   (b) a consistently high quality pizza product   *(4 marks)*

   (c) Why is it possible to deposit tomato purée, herbs and cheese by machine whilst the sliced fresh tomatoes have to be placed by hand?   *(2 marks)*

   (d) What are the advantages of freezing foods at a commercial temperature compared to a domestic freezer temperature?   *(2 marks)*

   (Total 12 marks)

2 Food packets give you a lot of information about the product. Some of this is required by law. The box below gives you some examples.

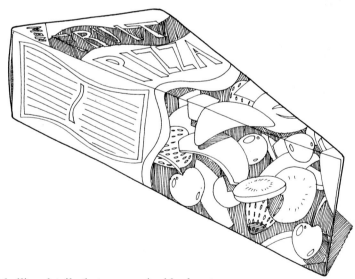

   (a) List three labelling details that are required by law to appear on prepacked foods.   *(3 marks)*

   (b) List two labelling details the manufacturer may add to a food label.   *(2 marks)*

   (c) (i) Suggest one suitable packaging material for the pizza, bearing in mind:
          • the food materials in the pizza product
          • the preservation method   *(2 marks)*
      (ii) Give two reasons why you would use this material.   *(4 marks)*

   (Total 11 marks)

Questions 3 and 4 are taken from the ULEAC Examination Board GCSE Specimen Paper. They deal with energy density in food, physical and chemical properties of food materials, marketing, packaging and storage of food products

3 Knowledge of the energy density of food is applied in the designed of food products to meet specific market forces.

(a) Explain the meaning of the term 'energy density'   *(2 marks)*

(b) The table below gives information relating to the energy density of a variety of foods.

Foods with a higher energy density kj per 100 g food		Foods with a lower energy density kj per 100 g food	
Digestive biscuits	1981	Boiled potatoes	343
Chips	1065	Fresh peaches	156
Canned peaches in syrup	373	Tomatoes	60
Avocado pear	922	Roast lean leg of pork	777
Fried port sausages	1317	Grilled lean rump steak	708
Fried beefburger	1099	Cooked haricot beans	396
Stewed minced beef	955	Wholemeal bread	918

Explain how the information in the table would be used in the development of a product targeted at middle aged people who wish to slim.   *(4 marks)*

(Total 6 marks)

4 Meringue cases are manufactured in volume to supply both retailers and caterers. The meringues are to be packed in sixes.

(a) (i) List SIX criteria that must be considered when designing the packaging.

     (6 marks)

   (ii) Choose THREE of your criteria given in answer to part (i) and give detailed reasons for including them in your list.   *(6 marks)*

(b) Give TWO chemical properties of egg white which make meringue manufacture possible.   *(2 marks)*

(c) (i) Name and briefly describe the process that is used to make meringue 'shapes' from a ready prepared meringue mixture.   *(3 marks)*

   (ii) Explain the differences between the way a small home caterer and an industrial manufacturer would carry out this process.   *(4 marks)*

(d) Meringues are often sold in supermarkets complete with fillings.

   (i) Give TWO different storage instructions that must be printed on a package of fresh cream meringues.   *(4 marks)*

   (ii) Explain ONE major commercial disadvantage a supermarket might experience from marketing fresh cream products.   *(2 marks)*

(Total 27 marks)

This question is from Northern Examinations and Assessment Board GCSE Specimen Paper. It deals with the function of food materials.

5 Below is a list of ingredients for a cook chill Tuna and Pasta Bake which serves two people.

2 carrots sliced
2 tablespoons plain wholemeal flour
2 celery sticks, sliced
2 tablespoon oil
1 onion, chopped
3 tablespoons wholemeal bread crumbs

175g (6oz) dried whole-wheat pasta
125g (4oz) Cheddar cheese, grated
125g (4oz) frozen peas
198g (7oz) can tuna, drained and flaked
300 ml (1/2 pint) milk (approx.)

The chart below gives the nutritional analysis of the recipe.
Using this information answer the questions which follow.

Type of food	Protein (g)	Fat (g)	Carbohydrate (g)	Fibre (g)	Energy
50g raw carrot	0.3	0.0	2.5	1.5	11 kcal/46 kJ
25g raw celery	0.2	0.0	0.3	0.5	2 kcal/ 9kJ
125g raw peas	7.5	0.5	13.7	6.2	88 kcal/ 371kJ
175g raw spaghetti	24.5	1.7	147.0	5.2	701 kcal/2937 kJ
25g vegetable oil	0.0	25.0	0.0	0.0	225 kcal/ 941kJ
25g raw onions	0.2	0.0	1.2	0.2	6 kcal/ 27kJ
50g brown flour	6.5	1.0	34.5	4.0	174 kcal/ 724kJ
300g milk	9.8	12.3	14.1	0.0	198 kcal/ 828kJ
198g canned tuna in oil	45.5	43.5	0.0	0.0	574 kcal/2403 kJ
125g Cheddar cheese (hard)	32.5	42 .5	0.0	0.0	512 kcal/2145 kJ
25g wholemeal bread	2.2	0.6	10.5	2.2	56 kcal/237 kJ
TOTAL nutrients in diet	129.2	126.1	223.8	19.8	2546 kcal/10666 kJ

How might the information be used during the development of the Tuna Pasta Bake in terms of :

(a) reducing the carbohydrate content ?   (3 marks)

(b) increasing the fibre content ?   (2 marks)

(c) reducing the fat content ?   (4 marks)

(d) marketing and selling the Tuna Pasta Bake as part of a healthy eating
      option ?   (2 marks)

(Total 11 marks)

General Case Studies

Designing our surroundings

Our surroundings and the buildings we live and work in play an important role in how we feel about ourselves, and the world we live in. People work better if they have an environment which is comfortable and stress free.

Architects design environments to help people work better. When designing a new building the architect will consider factors that affect people such as:

- the air they breath;
- the opening and closing windows;
- the temperature;
- the lighting, both natural and artificial;
- sources and level of noise;
- the closeness of other people.

Pause for thought

Try to remember an occasion when you felt uncomfortable in a room or building. What was it that made you feel that way?

Designed for work

When the architects were designing the Powergen building in Coventry they wanted to make it as energy efficient as possible as well as a good place to work. They decided to use a computer system to monitor the temperature, air flow and lighting. The computer uses the data it receives from sensors around the building to keep a constant check on all these things and to adjust them to save energy. It can open and close windows, turn on lights, etc. when the data it receives indicates that this is necessary. However, individual workers can override the computer, if they want to, at any time. This makes people feel happier because they are in control of their environment and the computer system is still able to save on wasted energy.

The architects were also asked to find ways to improve people's ability to work. Some modern buildings have been found to make people working there feel sick. **Sick Building Syndrome (SBS)** has been associated with factors such as air-conditioning systems, bad lighting and lack of building hygiene. Architects now know more about SBS and the subsequent rise in standards of materials handling during construction has largely eliminated SBS from new buildings today.

Questions

1 Make a list of the environmental factors that affect whether you can settle down to do your homework.

2 Make a list of the environmental factors that might affect whether an office worker can work efficiently.

3 Compare your two lists to identify the things they have in common.

◐ *The environment inside the Powergen Building is computer controlled*

Designed to prevent crime and vandalism

When the Docklands Light Railway was being designed the architects knew that the railway went through tough, crime-ridden areas of London and that many of the stations were to be unmanned during large parts of the day. Any solutions they proposed would need to meet three targets:

- prevent crime;
- improve passenger safety;
- require minimum maintenance and repair.

Very little glass is used in the station designs as glass is often vandalized and needs replacing regularly. All the materials used in the construction of the stations have been chemically treated to make graffiti easy to clean off.

R

Research activity

Make a sketch (or take a photograph) of a building, and its surroundings, that is poorly designed or misused. Add notes to show what is wrong. List some of the ways which would improve the environment for everyone living or working there.

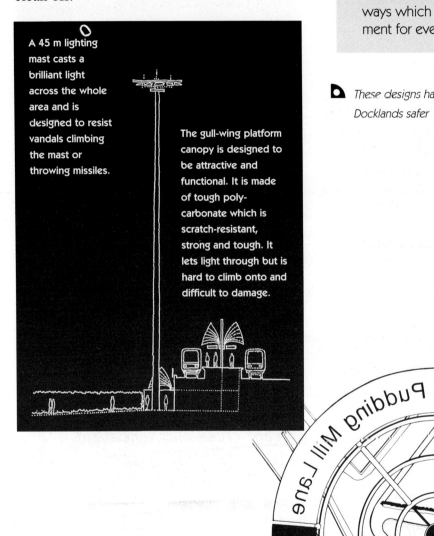

A 45 m lighting mast casts a brilliant light across the whole area and is designed to resist vandals climbing the mast or throwing missiles.

The gull-wing platform canopy is designed to be attractive and functional. It is made of tough poly-carbonate which is scratch-resistant, strong and tough. It lets light through but is hard to climb onto and difficult to damage.

These designs have helped make Docklands safer

Looking down from the top of the lighting mast note the thorny hedge next to the path that leads to the ticket booth. This protects passengers from ambush by muggers. The ticket booth is designed to resist ram raiding even by a JCB.

Designed to entertain

London's Planetarium is Europe's largest and the capital's major tourist attraction. Its large green dome in Marylebone Road is a familiar London landmark. The Planetarium presents a dramatic exploration of the solar system. It was built in 1956 but was not designed for the large numbers of visitors it now attracts – up to 14 000 per day in peak season.

The project for upgrading the Planetarium for the twenty-first century was well over due and it had to be completed in just 20 weeks to reduce the amount of time it was closed and to minimize disturbance to Madam Tussaud's.

The architects came up with a practical solution which retained all the drama and expectation associated with such an attraction.

The London Planetarium from the outside

The original round theatre seating has been replaced with seats facing in one direction only. The seats are now raked to give people a better view, and have been designed by computer to calculate accurately the sightlines for each seat.

A new Digistar laser projection system has been installed to provide state-of-the-art images.

The projection dome has been raised to allow more space underneath for people to queue inside the building and for a new floor to be inserted. This will reduce congestion on the pavements outside.

R Research activity

Take a trip to a local public attraction or entertainment venue. It can be a museum, cinema or theatre. Make a sketch or take some photographs and add notes to explain the following:

- how the building is laid out;
- how lighting and sound are used;
- how people are moved around the building.

From your observations make a list of possible improvements.

Curved corridors entice the visitor into the auditorium. The dramatic effect is enhanced by sound and lighting. This also keeps people moving, which is important when dealing with a large volume of people.

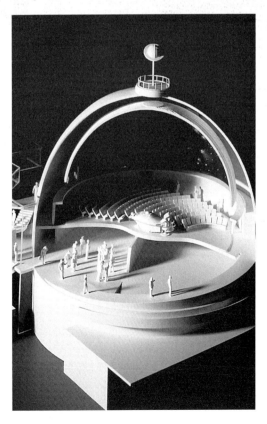

The new design for the inside of the London Planetarium

Information – the power to change lives

The way we communicate with other human beings and the speed with which we receive information have influenced dramatically the kind of world we live in today.

The start of books

Five hundred years ago most people were illiterate and relied upon word of mouth to receive information. Books were only available to closed religious orders and were laboriously copied by hand. In 1448 a German goldsmith, Johan Gutenberg, invented a way of printing whole pages using movable type. Gutenberg used this method to produce the first printed bible in 1456.

William Caxton was the first Englishman to develop a printing business. He printed his first book in the English language in 1474, called *The Recuyell of the Historie of Troye*.

Pause for thought

What is the possible connection between books becoming more widely available and schools opening?

As printing became faster, books were published on all sorts of subjects. As more books became available more people learned to read. It was also around this time that the first schools were opened.

How books shaped people's ideas

In France, the illegal and illicit distribution of cheaply printed books called 'Chap' books became commonplace by the late 1700s. One of these Chap books informed the ordinary people about the enormous excesses of the monarchy. Chap books helped to kindle a sense of national identity which ultimately lead to the French Revolution and the overthrow of the monarchy.

Pause for thought

Can you think of examples where the press is criticized for printing stories about royalty ?

Information from books added to the resentment that caused the French Revolution

Information becomes important for business

In 1605, the year of the Gunpowder Plot, the first newspaper was printed, in Antwerp, Holland. The first British newspaper was called the *Daily Courant* and first appeared in 1702. At that time newspapers were read mainly by businessmen and merchants because they contained stories from other parts of the world which were important to trade and politics.

Questions

Working in a group discuss the following.

1 With new industry new jobs develop. What jobs do you think were created to operate the newspaper industry?

2 How do you think newspapers got their news two centuries ago as compared with today?

3 a Who decides what news is printed in the newspapers?

  b What might influence their decisions?

Pause for thought

Despite technological advances news is still passed on by word of mouth today. Journalists often interview on-the-spot witnesses or experts before writing up the stories for the newspapers.

New inventions and discoveries for mass communication

By the end of the nineteenth century Sir Alexander Graham Bell, a Scottish scientist, had invented the telephone and Guglielmo Marconi had invented the radio. It was now possible to communicate rapidly with people across the world. Radio had such potential for mass communication that the government set up the British Broadcasting Company in 1922, later to become the British Broadcasting Corporation (BBC).

Radio made it possible for people to hear the voices of politicians and other important people for the first time. The people of Britain would have heard Neville Chamberlain's famous announcement that Britain was 'now at war with Germany' in September 1939 on the radio.

By the mid 1930s nearly every family had a radio – for many a major source of news and entertainment. Radio stars were as popular as pop stars are today

Radio with pictures

During the 1920s John Logie Baird, another British engineer, was working on the idea of talking pictures. The BBC immediately became interested in his idea and started to develop television, transmitting its first programme in 1929. However it was not until the coronation of Queen Elizabeth II was televised in 1953 that large numbers of people hired TV sets and started to watch television regularly.

In the 1970s satellite communications were developed so pictures could be transmitted as they happened from anywhere in the world.

Pause for thought

How much time do you spend each day listening to the radio and watching television?

Questions

Working in a group discuss the following.

4 Do you think that television and radio have changed our lives for the better or the worse?

5 Do you think television influences people's opinions?

6 Do you think it right that the government can censor what we watch?

Mass communication has changed our lives forever

Television is thought to have a very strong influence on people because of its power to shape our thoughts and ideas. The government regulates what we see on television and has the right to veto a programme if it thinks the content is not in the national interest.

At first there was only one channel and pictures were transmitted in black and white. By the 1960s ITV, the first commercial channel, had been given a licence to broadcast and later, in the mid 1960s, colour was introduced

▶ *Reporters covering wars, the World Cup or the Olympic Games all use satellite communications, so we can see events as they happen, wherever they are taking place in the world*

Information is power

Today almost everyone needs information for work, leisure, education and for the day-to-day running of our lives. We can access the information we need very quickly, almost instantly in some cases, through using information technology. A single CD ROM can hold the information of many encyclopaedias, and high street banks' on-line computers can give instant information about personal finances at cash points throughout the country.

Having relevant information enables people to make decisions and to have more control over their lives. By using computers, phone lines and satellite links, the Internet allows people to exchange ideas and information with anyone in the world. It lets people communicate cheaply and rapidly without the information being edited or censored by a publisher, broadcaster or government. Communication via the Internet is a two-way process, meaning that anyone who transmits information on the Internet can have a dialogue with whoever receives the information anywhere in the world.

▶ *Using a CD ROM to access information*

DIY medical testing

Some products could not be designed if the designers didn't understand the science behind the way the product works. Obvious examples are motor cars, radios and televisions, microwave ovens and thermal blankets. The science behind these products is mainly physics and chemistry. Now new medical products are being developed which depend on an understanding of biology. For example, in the past a doctor would test for diabetes by sticking a finger into a sample of urine and licking it to see if it tasted sweet. Nowadays the doctor would use a chemical test strip developed specially to test for sugar.

 Old-style medical tesing

Some medical tests are so simple and reliable that anyone can carry them out. A new type of product has therefore come onto the market – do-it-yourself medical testing kits.

P

Pause for thought

What medical conditions might people want to test themselves for?

Testing for pregnancy

When a woman becomes pregnant she produces a chemical called human chorionic gonadotrophin (hCG). This chemical is present in a woman's urine when she is pregnant. In order to find out if she is pregnant, therefore, a woman can test for hCG in her urine.

Until fairly recently the only way to test for hCG was to inject the urine sample into a female animal such as a mouse or toad. If hCG was present then the woman's urine would cause the animal to produce eggs. If she was not pregnant there would be no hCG so no eggs would be produced. This test had many disadvantages:

● it had to be carried out by a laboratory technician;

● it took several days;

● sometimes the animals had to be killed to find out if eggs had been produced.

Biologists have discovered that our white blood cells produce antibodies as part of our defence system against attack by viruses, bacteria and certain chemicals, generally called antigens. The antibodies protect us by recognizing and combining with the antigens and rendering them harmless. The white blood cells produce particular antibodies to fight particular antigens.

In 1975 two scientists discovered how to produce large amounts of antibodies outside the body in a fermenter. This enabled scientists to produce a wide range of antibodies in large quantities, including one that could recognize and combine with hCG and nothing else. They knew this could form the basis of a reliable and accurate pregnancy test. Now it was up to product designers to develop an easy-to-use pregnancy testing kit.

Here's what they developed …

 The Clearblue One-step pregnancy testing kit

The pregnancy testing kit

To carry out the test a woman urinates onto the absorbent sampler.

There are two windows in the test kit. A blue line appears in the smaller of the two windows to show that the test is complete and has worked correctly. If the rest is positive a line will appear in the large window, showing that the user is pregnant.

How it works

How the test kit works is explained below.

 R Research activity

Find out the meanings of the following terms:
monoclonal antibodies
hybridoma cells.

Q Questions

1 Why is the small window important?

2 Why is urine used for the test rather than blood?

3 a What are the advantages for a woman in knowing that she is pregnant as soon as possible after she has conceived?

b Are there any disadvantages in knowing as soon as possible?

4 Why is it important for the test to be reliable and accurate?

5 Why is it important for the test to be easy to use?

6 What changes would you make to the test kit if it were to be used in a hospital laboratory?

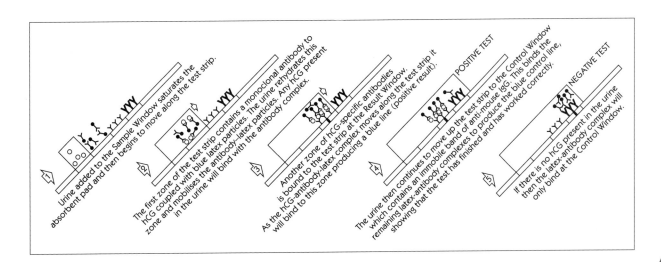

1 Urine added to the Sample Window saturates the absorbent pad and then begins to move along the test strip.

2 The first zone of the test strip contains a monoclonal antibody to hCG coupled with blue latex particles. The urine rehydrates this zone and mobilises the antibody–latex particles. Any hCG present in the urine will bind with the antibody complex.

3 Another zone of hCG-specific antibodies is bound to the test strip at the Result Window. As the hCG-antibody-latex complex moves along the test strip it will bind to this zone producing a blue line (positive result).

POSITIVE TEST

4 The urine then continues to move up the test strip to the Control Window which contains an immobile band of anti-mouse IgG. This binds the remaining latex–antibody complexes to produce the blue control line, showing that the test has finished and has worked correctly.

NEGATIVE TEST

5 If there is no hCG present in the urine then the latex-antibody complex will only bind at the Control Window.

Manufacturing aircraft

Since 1901, when the American Orville Wright made the first flight in a powered aircraft, the aerospace industry has come a long way. Early pioneers, sometimes working in garden sheds, built their flying machines out of linen and wood – during World War I furniture factories were enlisted to meet the demand for aircraft parts.

By World War II most aircraft were made of aluminium alloy, and it was car factories which turned to aircraft manufacture. Since then the development of passenger aeroplanes and increasingly sophisticated technology have transformed the aerospace industry. It is now vast, encompassing the design and manufacture of military and civil aircraft ranging from microlights and gliders to Concorde.

Pause for thought

Why do you think it was car factories not furniture factories that made aircraft in World War II?

Multinational manufacture

Every aeroplane is made up of thousands of different parts or components, all of which have to be functioning perfectly to ensure the efficiency and durability of the aircraft, and the safety and comfort of its passengers.

From the engine and wings to the door handles and headrests, every component has to be painstakingly designed, developed, tested and made. Because of the enormous amount of work involved, the parts to make one aeroplane are often produced in different factories all over the world before coming together for final assembly as shown below.

Designing and making the wing flaps

Shorts is one of Britain's oldest and largest aircraft manufacturers. It has been in the flight business since 1901, when Oswald and Eustace Short started making aerial balloons. Today Shorts employs 7800 people in the design, development and manufacture of a wide range of aircraft and aerostructures (aircraft components).

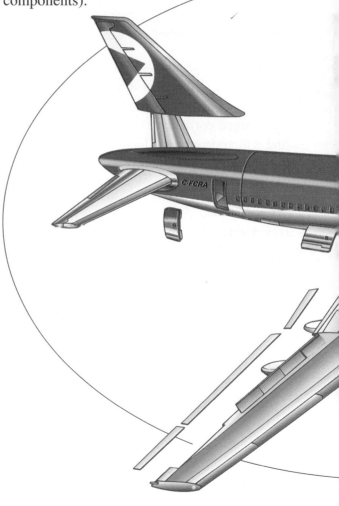

Shorts' aircraft and aerostructures are designed by Aero Designs Ltd on the Isle of Man. This is a special part of the company dedicated to designing aerostructures ready for manufacture and assembly at Shorts' sites. The designing is carried out using **computer-aided design (CAD)**. The results can be plotted out as 2D drawings, 3D wire frames or surface envelopes. From the design drawings the computer can calculate surface areas and volumes, and carry out stress analysis. All the members of the design team are networked to each other so that they can take into account how the others' designs are developing. For example, changes in the design of a wing will almost certainly require changes in the design of the wing flaps.

Once the final design for the wing flaps is complete and the designers are satisfied that it meets the specification, the information needed to manufacture the parts is sent via a telephone line to the manufacturing site in Belfast. The information is fed directly into computer-controlled machines which can then be set to work to make the parts. This process of designing and manufacturing with the aid of computers is called **CAD/CAM** (computer-aided design/computer-aided manufacture). Once the parts are made they can be assembled into the completed wing flap which is sent to the USA for inclusion in the aeroplane.

Research activity

Find out if there are any manufacturing companies in your area. Make a list of them. Find out which ones use CAD to design their products, and which ones use CAM to make their products.

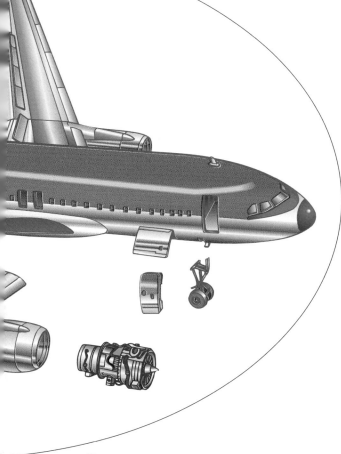

Parts for this airplane are made all over the world and assembled in the USA

CAD/CAM in action producing parts for a Boeing 757

Public transport In London

The early Victorians had rutted and cobbled streets with poor drainage and no road system as such. Today we have crowded buses, trains and tubes as well as an increasing number of vehicles creating more pollution and slowing traffic down. Are today's London residents and commuters any better off than their Victorian predecessors?

▶ *Early victorian scene*

Horses galore

The horse has played a key role in the development of public transport systems in cities across Europe. In 1829 the first regular horse bus service – carrying just 12 people – provided a fixed route service from the City of London to Paddington. It ran every three hours with a fare of one shilling (5p). This was a considerable sum of money at the time and so the service catered mainly for the wealthy. Its success encouraged other operators to set up services on other routes. This was the beginning of London's public transport system.

P **Pause for thought**

What is the future for public transport in London or any of Britain's other major cities?

Competition and cobbled streets

More operators in the market-place meant they had to compete for passengers. This made operators invest in ways of carrying more people. This resulted in the introduction of back-to-back seating on the tops of buses in 1850. These seats were accessed by a ladder – it took another 30 years to get a proper stairway to the top of the horse-drawn bus!

The size of the bus and therefore the number of passengers it could carry was limited by the power of the horses. A significant advance was made in 1861 with the introduction of horse-drawn trams. These had wheels which ran on steel tracks laid in the road. This made it easier for the horses to pull their loads which meant that buses could be made larger or more passengers could be carried on the existing buses.

▶ *Travelling 1870*

Trams provided a cheaper form of transport with lower fares. This meant that more people could afford to use them to get to and from work. By 1900 many suburban areas of London were served by tram routes.

Powering the way forward

In 1906 there were around 50 000 horses working in London, transporting more than 2 000 000 people per day. But the days of horse-drawn transport were numbered. Towards the end of the nineteenth century operators explored other power sources, such as steam, electricity and diesel fuel. Their aim was to become more competitive by making their vehicles either faster or able to carry more passengers. Experiments with steam-powered trams were short lived and electricity proved to be the ideal power source. From 1901 overhead power lines or road-embedded conduit systems were installed.

The main problem with electric trams was that they were not very manoeuvrable. The power lines and tracks were often laid down the middle of the road. People had to dodge the traffic passing on either side to get on the tram!

Horses could not compete with these clean, quiet, reliable and larger capacity vehicles, and with the simultaneous introduction of the diesel motor bus, the horse's demise was complete.

◘ *The trolley bus: more manoeuvrable than the tram because it did not need rails*

Trolley buses were introduced in London in the 1930s. They had already been used successfully in other cities for over two decades. They did not run on rails, though they were powered using overhead electric cables in a similar way to the trams. This meant they were more flexible as their manoeuvrability was limited only by the reach of their overhead power links. After World War II, from 1945 onwards the diesel-powered motor bus became the dominant form of public transport above ground and trolley buses ceased operation in London in 1962.

◘ *London electric tram in 1908*

General case studies

Going underground

London pioneered the underground railway system. It began with railway carriages pulled by a steam engine in 1863. This system was dirty and noisy and was replaced in 1890 by a deep-level electric system – the first in the world. Most of the central part of London's existing underground system was developed between the two wars, the outer reaches being developed after World War II. The London Underground is still being developed today with links to the Docklands Light Railway and the Jubilee line extension to the south of the River Thames.

Back above ground

The tram has not been totally forgotten. European cities such as Amsterdam have operated tram systems successfully for many decades and cities in England are beginning to follow suit. Manchester and Sheffield

Question

1   As public transport became more comprehensive, reliable and affordable, London changed. People could consider living further away from their workplace, knowing that they could get to work by public transport.

What effect do you think this had on the areas surrounding London and in the Victorian slum sites within the city?

launched new tram systems in the early 1990s. London Transport is exploring the possibility of a Tramlink between Wimbledon and Croydon using existing rail lines. As a virtually emission-free form of transport and one that can maximize the use of rechargeable power sources, tram systems are an attractive proposition for congested and polluted cities.

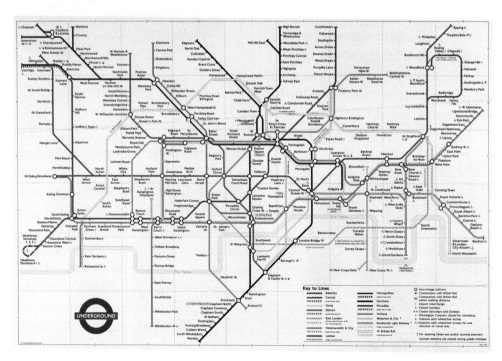

The modern tube map, first designed in 1933, shows only the sequence of stations and the connections

Ownership and intervention

Until the end of the nineteenth century individuals or companies owned various bus and tram routes. In 1891 London City Council started buying tramway companies and by 1899 they owned seven of the largest operations. By doing this the council was able to ensure that transport routes met the needs of the areas they served and the tram became the cornerstone of a public-owned transport system.

In 1933 the London Passenger Transport Board, a public body, was set up with powers to take over all bus, tram, trolley buses and underground services in London and adjacent counties. Today, bus routes are being offered for sale to private companies to manage. London Transport reported in 1994 'substantial savings of 15–20 per cent of previous operational costs … achieved from the tendering process.'

By the year 2001 it is planned that all bus routes will have been put out to tender to private companies. Over a period of 100 years public transport in London will have gone almost full circle, from private to public ownership and then back again.

Installing and managing the system

Public transport in London calls on all aspects of design and technology – civil engineering, mechanical and electrical engineering, large-scale manufacturing, advanced data capture and information handling systems, extensive maintenance and staff development.

London Transport has used the latest electronic and information technology to develop ticket vending machines and ticket reading machines linked to entry/exit points.

R **Research activity**

Find out about the public transport in your area. Try to answer these questions:

1 What are the bus routes?

2 How frequently do the buses run?

3 What is the cost of a journey from the outskirts to the city centre?

4 What concessions are available?

You might present your information in the form of a display including an annotated map.

Modern designs keep improving transport in London

The 'look' of London Transport has been developed through corporate identity programmes that cover signage, uniforms, livery for vehicles, promotional materials and stationery.

Technological endeavours

Success or failure – pushing back the barriers

Throughout history scientists, designers and engineers have striven to push back the boundaries of invention and discovery. What is it that compels them? What are their efforts really worth? Often struggling against public opinion and a lack of resources, their achievements can have important effects on people's lives. Their failures often attract ridicule and scorn.

Not all research is carried out with a particular end result in mind – some research is purely academic. Designers and technologists can build on and adapt another person's discovery, creating a new product, system or material which was previously unimagined. It is often the long-term potential of design and technological endeavours, rather than the immediate results, that are of the greatest significance.

Man walks on the moon – the culmination of years of endeavour

The space race

When American astronauts first walked on the surface of the moon in 1969, the event was heralded as a great achievement and the successful culmination of years of research, experimentation, testing and expense. But *why* did America want to put a man on the moon? Some see it as a struggle between the USA and the former USSR, each trying to prove that its political system produced the best technology. Once on the moon the astronauts took measurements and collected 400 kg of rock samples.

Q Questions

1 For each of the following highly successful products write down what the designer or inventor needed to know about to develop a successful design:

 a Post-it
 b PrittStick
 c Tipp-Ex.

 P Pause for thought

It cost many millions of dollars for America to win the space race. Was it worth it?

The real value of the space race was, however, far more long term and influential. By landing a craft on the moon scientists discovered how to manoeuvre vehicles successfully in space. This led to further research which eventually produced satellites. Satellites now play a key role in people's everyday lives. Satellite-based telecommunications systems provide up-to-the-minute news, current affairs, entertainment and education via television pictures, radio and telephone links across the world. Navigation between countries and continents has been improved by the use of satellite information. Weather forecasts would not be nearly so accurate or informative without data capture by satellite.

Space race technology has allowed space stations to be placed in orbit around the Earth where research into solar energy, medicine and industrial processes are carried out. These experiments in turn could have unplanned and unpredicted far-reaching results.

R

Research activity

Find out what other 'spin-offs' there have been from the space race. Make a list and give each one a star rating for how useful it is.

One good thing leads to another

Scientists do not always reap the full benefits of their endeavours; once the purpose of their research is achieved, the project comes to an end. The further exploration and exploitation of the potential of each new development is often taken up by designers and technologists operating in other fields.

Teflon

One material used in the development of spacecraft provides a good example of how designers and engineers can pick up and adapt other scientists' discoveries.

In 1938 an American scientist working on refrigerants for DuPont, Dr Roy Plunkett, discovered a new material which he called Teflon, or polytetrafluoroethylene (PTFE). It had many unique qualities:

- resistance to high temperatures;
- very low conductivity;
- a very slippery surface;
- non-reaction with other chemicals.

However its commercial potential was not fully explored until 1954. Then a Frenchman, Marc Gregoire, used some PTFE to lubricate his fishing tackle and realized that the material could be spread over the base of a frying pan to create a non-stick surface.

The Tefal non-stick cookware company grew out of this discovery. Teflon later became an integral and important component of the spacecrafts sent to the moon – its resistance to high temperatures was essential for successful re-entry into the Earth's atmosphere.

In the 1990s Teflon is used by textile designers as a protective coating for garments. By applying a layer of Teflon to clothes it ensures that they are waterproof, breathable and stain repellent.

Pause for thought

What could the next application of Teflon be?

Microwaves

The development of microwaves also demonstrates how one achievement can be adapted and applied by other people. In 1940 two British physicists, Sir John Randall and Dr H A Boot, developed the magnetron, an electronic tube which produced microwave energy, for use in radar installations. It then contributed successfully towards Britain's war defences. Microwaves are radio waves less than 30 cm in length. They can be focused easily into a sharp beam which reduces the chances of interference from other transmitters.

It was the Americans and Japanese who explored the wider potential of microwaves in the domestic market-place. At one radar installation an American manufacturer called Percy Le Baron Spencer noticed the heat given off by a magnetron's electronic tube. He tested the strength of this heat by putting a paper bag full of maize into the field of the tube. Within seconds the maize swelled and burst, and Percy had perfect popcorn!

Spencer's firm, Raytheon, realized the commercial potential of the magnetron and set about developing a cooker operated by an electronic tube. Microwaves penetrate food to a depth of 50 mm and cause the water molecules in the food to vibrate rapidly. This makes the food hot.

The first Raytheon microwave ovens were large and heavy units meant for big users like hospitals and canteens. The technology continued to be developed and refined and the first household ovens were produced by the Japanese Tappan company. Microwave ovens are now one of the most highly desirable and widely available consumer items.

Questions

2 Make a list of some of the products you use every day. For each one write down the technologies that it uses.

The value of failures

Many technological endeavours result in failure. Not every design development can be a success, whether instant or long term, but the research and ideas that led up to the 'failure' can still be used and adapted.

Sometimes developments do not succeed because of the influence of direct competition. VHS and Betacam became available to consumers at the same time, and only one, VHS, survived in the market-place.

Sometimes designs are not taken up because the public is simply not ready for the idea.

Ultimately some ideas fail because they simply do not work. This does not make the endeavour worthless – other designers can learn from the mistakes and avoid them.

Research activity

Some of the most exciting technological developments in the future will depend on advances in our understanding of biology, particularly genetics. Find out about genetic engineering and suggest some products and services that may be based on this.

Focused Case Studies

Wrap it up

The packaging of food products has five main functions:

- to protect the products from damage;
- to keep them clean and fit to eat (hygiene);
- to extend their shelf-life;
- to market them effectively;
- to provide nutritional information and instructions as required by law.

The wrapping of food products has changed dramatically over the last 50 years. The changes in the packaging of bread, potatoes, eggs and biscuits are shown in the table below.

Research activity

Fresh eggs clearly present a packaging challenge, and even within one supermarket you may find more than one sort of packaging being used. You can investigate the effectiveness of various types of packaging through the following activities.

1 Collect a range of different egg boxes.

2 Make a quick annotated drawing of each box labelling the material used, the marketing information and the legally required information.

3 Devise some simple tests to find out which of the boxes protects eggs the best. Present your results graphically.

Question

Look carefully at the information in the table. Discuss it with another student and try to identify a trend in the way that food packaging has developed.

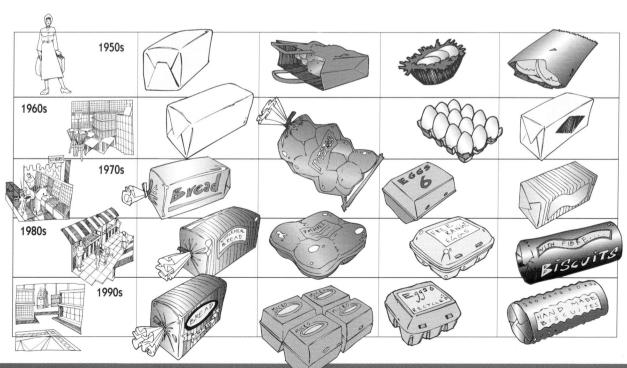

Focused case studies

The advantages of see-through

Clear (transparent) packaging is obviously useful because you are able to see easily what you are buying. One major type of transparent packaging is plastic film. There are now plastic films that can be used for a wide range of products as shown opposite.

The main plastic films used for packaging are shown in the panel below.

▶ *Some packaging using see-through plastic film*

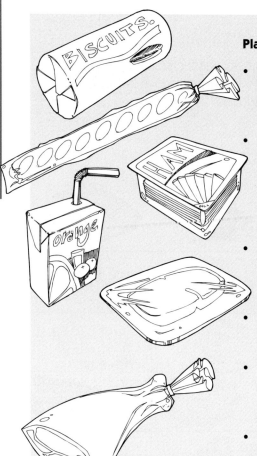

Plastic film

- *Polypropylene film*
  This can be uncoated, non-sealable and have a treated side for printing. It is transparent, strong, and puncture and tear resistant.

- *Cellulose film*
  This is used for 'niche' applications mainly in twist wrapping and where a semi-permeable film is necessary to allow moisture loss at a controlled rate. This film is static-free, easy to tear, easy to release from sealing, a good odour, gas and water barrier, readily printable and biodegradable.

- *Polyester film (PET)*
  This is used for laminations, mainly because it adds strength and gloss, resists distortion and is easy to heat seal.

- *Polyolefin film*
  Easy-to-peel polythene; it is used when a peelable seal is required.

- *Nylon film*
  This is used for deep-freeze packaging of awkward shapes as it is flexible and resists cracking.

- *PVC film*
  Unplasticized PVC is used for thermoforming.

But is it safe?

Food protection is the prime concern of the manufacturers of ready-to-eat food. The implications of food being tainted, smelly or containing poisonous or harmful substances are extremely serious, both for the manufacturer and for the consumer's health and well-being. So hygiene and cleanliness are key issues. Plastic films, whether as containers or covers, seem ideal. However, there is one problem associated with them. Some substances can 'migrate' from the packaging into the food and therefore into the consumer. If the substance involved is a volatile chemical, it can cause 'taint' which is present only as a smell. It may be too small to quantify and is never harmful. However, it does detract from the product and is not acceptable to most consumers.

The problems with using plastic film are not as straightforward as you might think. The simplest is shown in diagram 1 opposite. One of the materials used in the packaging migrates from the packaging into the food. Another possibility, shown in the second diagram, is that an impurity is in the starting materials used to make the packaging. It is only present in very low concentrations but migrates into the food. The chance of this happening might be higher than you expect because the impurity could be much more soluble in food than the main packaging material.

A third possibility (diagram 3) is that the very process of producing the packaging generates a compound which was not present in the starting materials and that this contaminates the food. This is a tricky one to detect because unless you suspect this possibility you wouldn't begin to look for it.

A fourth possibility (diagram 4) is that the food reacts with the packaging to generate an impurity.

Finally, the digestive system of the consumer might react to a packaging material impurity and turn it into yet another impurity which may be harmful (diagram 5).

As you may imagine, there is extensive and complex research being undertaken into what chemicals might be ingested by the consumer and the consequences of that ingestion.

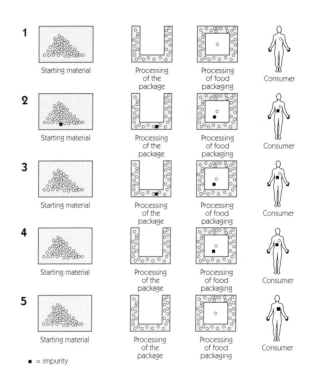

■ = impurity

Ⓡ Research activity

To make sure that you have a basic understanding of plastics, check with your science teacher about the meanings of these terms:

monomer	polymer
polymerization	thermoplastic
thermosetting plastic.	

Soup, beautiful soup

New Covent Garden Soup Company

The New Covent Garden Soup Company was set up to manufacture soup that is as good as home-made, prepared with only natural ingredients with no preservatives, colourings or additives. The patented production process is unique and took two years to develop! The ideas for the first 30 types of soup initially came from employees, and were primarily vegetable. They were cooked as samples and modified until the recipe pleased most people. Now the company has extended its range to include meat and fish. The 'home-made', all-year-round range is complemented by summer and winter specials that are based on seasonal vegetables. The company also makes a soup-of-the-month, a clever idea to introduce new and unusual flavours to the market.

The label is stuck on so the basic carton can be used for any type of soup

P Pause for thought

Do you like soup? What is your favourite flavour? How often do you eat it? Would you say it is a snack or a meal?

R Research activity

Tomato is the most popular flavour of tinned soup. Why do you think that is? Is it the most popular flavour in your class? You can find out like this. Copy out the table below. Working in a group of six complete the table.

Person	Do you like soup?	Which is your favourite flavour?	When do you eat it?	Which of the following sorts do you eat?			
				homemade	tinned	dried	chilled carton
A: You							
B							
C							
D							
E							
F							

Scale of production

Developing a recipe for home-made soup that works in the kitchen is one thing – manufacturing soups on a large scale is another!

Scale makes a difference

To assure the quality of its product, the New Covent Garden Soup Company monitors the quality of the starting ingredients, the preparation, weighing and preliminary cooking of those ingredients, the cooking of the soup, and the filling, sealing and date stamping of the cartons.

The soup is cooked in large sealed tanks. The partially cooked ingredients are transferred to the tanks and extra milk and cream are then pumped into the tank through pipes. The total amount of these ingredients and their rate of addition can be carefully controlled. Steam is passed into the tank to heat the ingredients, and air is pumped in to aerate and agitate them. The pressure and temperature within the tank are monitored and kept within strict limits as is the weight of the mixture in the tank.

The exact details of the process are a carefully guarded industrial secret, but clearly it requires a sophisticated, automated manufacturing system that senses and controls weight, pressure, temperature and time. The system uses computer control and operators can check on progress and on the cooking conditions by information presented on monitors.

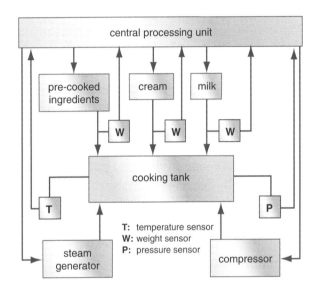

A simplified systems diagram for automated bulk soup production

Questions

1 The New Covent Garden Soup Company uses the following ingredients for their white bean with tomato and sage soup:

water; tomatoes; white beans; milk; cream; onions; tomato purée; vegetable stock; butter; brown sugar; sage; salt; garlic.

For each of these ingredients suggest a quality assurance procedure that could be carried out to ensure that it is suitable for use in bulk soup production.

Packaging the soup

Once the soup is cooked it is piped to a machine which automatically opens out the flat-pack cartons and fills them with soup. The temperature of the soup is kept at between 70°C and 83°C during this process. The cartons are then sealed and date stamped. Quality control at this point rejects any cartons not properly sealed or stamped. The soup is sold from the chilled section of supermarkets.

Where do the cartons come from and what are they made of?

The cartons used are Pure-Pak® cartons made by Elopack. The cartons are made from a laminate – a series of thin film materials stuck together (see opposite). The outer polythene coating provides a barrier to moisture preventing any water getting into the soup from the outside. The cardboard provides strength. It is made from wood pulp that has been specially bleached to remove impurities such as lignin and resins which can affect the taste of fresh packed food. The surlyn is a tough plastic that acts as an adhesive, bonding the aluminium foil to the board. The aluminium foil acts as a barrier preventing the soup from touching and weakening the board.

The cartons are delivered to the New Covent Garden Soup Company packed flat. The machine that fills the cartons with soup has to open out the carton, seal up the bottom, fill the carton with soup and seal it.

Questions

2 Why do you think the temperature of the soup is kept at 70–83°C while the cartons are being filled?

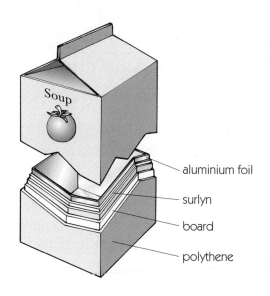

D *The layers in a Pure-Pak® carton used for soup.*

- aluminium foil
- surlyn
- board
- polythene

Research activity

A wide range of containers is used to hold liquid foods and drinks. Use this activity to find out more about them. Find five different sorts of packaging for liquids in the supermarket and describe them using the following table. One example is filled in already.

Food product	Type of packaging	Materials used	Access to the product
vinegar	bottle	glass for bottle; plastic for cap and nozzle	remove screw on cap and shake out through nozzle

A corny story

Popcorn and sweetcorn are two familiar processed cereal products. They look quite similar but are produced from two different types of maize. Popcorn is made from a type of maize that has been selected for its ability to 'pop' when heated. Sweetcorn is a maize that is harvested while still immature for canning, freezing or eating as corn on the cob when it has been boiled. Maize is the second most-grown cereal crop in the world, grown in every continent except Antarctica! The reason it is grown so extensively is because it is extremely useful.

P

Pause for thought

How many different products can you think of that come from maize? Check out your answer with the illustration below.

R

Research activity

You can use this activity to find out more about how maize is processed. Collect samples of corn, flaked maize, maize flour, corn oil and two or three brands of cereal. Write a description of each one listing the processes involved in its production. Put your samples in order of the amount of processing, starting with the least.

The birth of a cornflake

How does the seed of a maize plant become a cornflake? Over 100 years ago Dr John Kellogg, a vegetarian and health food specialist, developed grain food products to replace meat- and fish-based meals. He mixed grits (pieces of corn endosperm) with flavoured syrup, rolled and toasted them, boxed them, and the rest is history! But there is a huge difference between making small batches of products and the multi-million industry that breakfast cereals have become – most supermarkets stock over 100 different types!

The cornflake story

There are many stages in the manufacture of cornflakes. Remember it is only the grit from the grain that becomes flaked! The process is described in the panel below.

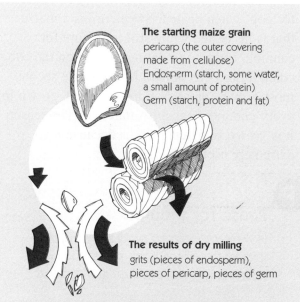

The starting maize grain
pericarp (the outer covering made from cellulose)
Endosperm (starch, some water, a small amount of protein)
Germ (starch, protein and fat)

The results of dry milling
grits (pieces of endosperm), pieces of pericarp, pieces of germ

Stage 1 Dry milling

The maize is tempered with water to a moisture level of 18–24 per cent. This toughens the grit and makes it swell so that it is easier to separate from the germ and pericarp. The milling cracks open the maize grain so that the grit breaks free. The grit is separated from the other fragments by sieving, aerating, gravity-separating and roller milling. The larger flaking grits are used in the production of flaked breakfast cereals.

Stage 2 Mixing and cooking

The separated grits are now mixed with various colourings and flavourings such as sugar, salt and malt. Cooking is done in batches. A rotating horizontal cylinder containing a syrup solution and the grits is used, tumbling and steaming them for up to two hours. A moisture content of 30–50 per cent is aimed for in this blending process. The cooking is complete when each grit has changed from a hard, chalky, white lump to a larger, soft, translucent, light golden brown particle. Properly cooked particles are rubbery but firm. Any uncooked parts show up in the finished flakes as white spots.

Stage 3 Dumping

The cooked cereal is now dumped onto a moving conveyor belt to cool (which stops the cooking action) and to spread the cereal out uniformly so that it can be fed into the dryer and cooler.

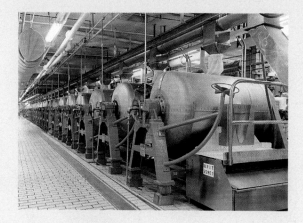

Stage 4 De-lumping

The cooked grits are stuck together in a loose mass after the cooking. They need to be broken into single grit particles so that each grit can dry uniformly. Most systems use screening devices – gyrating sifters, rotating wire or perforated drum screeners.

Stage 5 Drying

Once the grits are exposed to the air they lose moisture. It is important that the grits dry uniformly. If a surface skin is produced this stops moisture loss from the centre and you get soft-centred cornflakes! To prevent 'skinning', the drying conditions – temperature, humidity and airflow – are carefully controlled. Moisture has now been reduced to 10–14 per cent.

Stage 6 Cooling and tempering

Cooling is essential, as otherwise the grits would darken. They must be brought down to room temperature quickly. An unheated section of the dryer is often used for this. The grits are then stored in large bins to make sure that the moisture content both between and inside the particles is the same. This is called tempering.

Stage 7 Flaking

The cooked whole grain pieces are now flaked between very large, smooth, cooled, flaking rollers. They are flattened to a thickness of 2–4 mm and spread out. The moisture content here is crucial as there needs to be just enough moisture in the flake to expand when heated and turn the soggy, squashed lump into a crisp, light, crunchy cornflake.

Stage 8 Toasting

Toasting follows flaking and brings out the characteristic flavour, crisp texture and blistered surface of the finished flake. It is done in hot-air ovens and takes 1–4 minutes. Flake-toasting ovens are usually rotating drums; the flakes are toasted by hot air while they are suspended in mid-air in the oven. The colour is monitored visually by the oven operators and also by means of a colour-matching meter. Moisture content is also monitored.

R **Research activity**

You can use this activity to investigate the cost of breakfast cereals. In a group of six, list as many breakfast cereals as possible (use your nearest supermarket for reference). Put your list into groups depending on their cereal base. Compare cost per 100 g. Identify the cheapest and most expensive cereal in each group. Present your findings graphically. Try to explain the differences.

Copper and you

The Department of Health produces nutritional information on different substances in the form of Dietary Reference Values (DRVs), Estimated Average Requirements (EARs) and Recommended Nutrient Intakes (RNIs). To obtain this information on any substance, considerable research has to be carried out. This Case Study is about the research that is being planned to find out about the element copper.

What is it?

Copper is a transition metal and appears in the same group of the Periodic Table as silver and gold. It is an essential trace element in our diet. If it is not present in sufficient quantities, copper deficiency can result in loose skin, loose joints, anaemia and coronary artery disease. It is found in a variety of foods such as liver, nuts, prawns and wheat products.

These foods contain copper

Pause for thought

Write down everything you ate yesterday. Does your list include any of the foods mentioned above that contain copper?

Copper is a component of many of the metallo-enzymes that we need for essential body processes. Enzymes are biological catalysts. They speed up chemical reactions taking place in living cells. The roles of some metallo-enzymes containing copper are summarized below.

Copper-containing enzyme	What it does
cytochrome c oxidase	important for respiration (electron transport in mitochondria)
copper zinc superoxide dismutase	an antioxidant found in red blood cells
lysyl oxidase	links collagen and elastin
caeruloplasmin	enables iron to be processed for haemoglobin in the blood

Research activity

You can use this activity to find out about the treatments for vitamin deficiency diseases. Copy out and fill in the table, then choose one deficiency and describe it in detail.

Vitamin	Symptoms of deficiency	When discovered	Action taken
A			
B			
C			
D			
K			

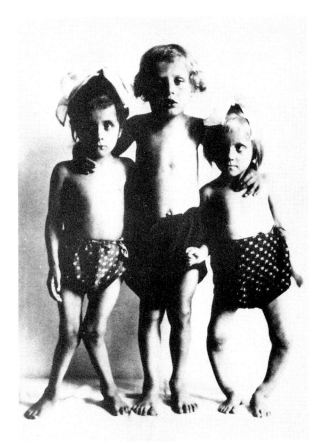

Lack of vitamin D causes rickets – a disease that was prevalent in the 1940s

Deficiency diseases

Historically, governments have intervened in the nation's diet when deficiencies have been proved to cause ill-health.

Sailors in the eighteenth century were issued with a ration of lime juice when it was realized that the scurvy they suffered from was due to a lack of vitamin C in their diet. Americans called English sailors 'limeys' because they drank lime juice, and this name has become American slang for an English person. In the 1940s and 50s, it was discovered that many children's diets were deficient and free National Health Service milk, orange juice and vitamins were issued. The government now recommends that we eat a balanced diet, and publishes Reference Nutrient Intake values (RNIs) for all vitamins. This value is the amount of a particular nutrient that is needed by almost every individual, even those with high needs. The table below shows the RNIs for a range of vitamins.

Vitamin	RNI for males, 15–18 years	RNI for females, 15–18 years
vitamin A	700 µg	600 µg
thiamin	1.1 mg	0.8 mg
vitamin B6	1.5 mg	1.2 mg
vitamin C	40 mg	40 mg

3

The need for accurate information

The Department of Health had difficulty in setting values for the amounts of copper needed in our diet. This requires further information from scientific studies. The setting of the values for copper is complicated by the fact that if a person has a marginally adequate copper diet that also contains a high intake of sucrose or fructose, then that person may display some of the symptoms of copper deficiency. It may be that the fructose interacts with the copper and might prevent its normal metabolism in the body.

In order to know more about copper in our diet, a major study is planned. The results will be used by the government to set values for copper in the diet. If copper deficiency was found to be a problem, then it may result in certain foods being fortified with copper, as in the case of iron in bread, although this is thought to be unlikely.

Research activity

Talk to your science teacher to find out how a mass spectrometer works. Make an annotated drawing explaining your findings.

Research into copper in our diet

Here is an outline of the dietary study that is being planned by the Institute of Food Research in Norwich.

Who will take part?	Male volunteers.
How much copper?	Their diets will contain high, medium and low levels of copper.
For how long?	8 weeks on the copper diet then a 4 week break.
What will be measured?	Cholesterol; copper zinc superoxide dismutase, caeruloplasmin; copper in the plasma; iron stores; haemoglobin.
How will the copper be measured?	A drink containing 3 mg of copper stable isotope (^{65}Cu) will be given after 8 weeks. During the following week, blood, urine and faeces samples taken. Mass spectrometry techniques will be used to follow the copper, e.g. is it in the blood; is it being excreted? The rate of the appearance of the copper will also be measured.
How will the research be organized?	Over a three year period: first year – planning, organization and recruiting the volunteers; next 18 months – residential dietary study; last 6 months – analysis of data and writing report.
What will happen then?	The government will use the information to help set accurate values for copper needed in our diet.

The study of copper in the diet is being carried out by Dr Linda Harvey at the Institute of Food Research in Norwich

Bread-making in Peru

Peru

Peru is a country of 21.7 million people situated on the west coast of Latin America. The geography and climate of the country are varied – on the western side the Andes mountains make it dry and barren while the Amazonian Basin in the east makes the climate subtropical and the countryside green and lush. The capital of the country is Lima, which is situated on the west coast.

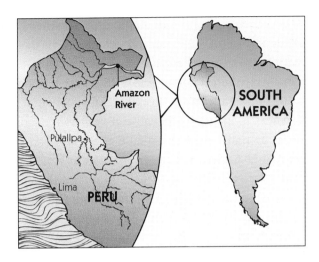

The Shipibo-Conibo indians

Pucallpa is the capital of the lower Amazonian region. It is a main river port and around 120 000 people live there. The river provides the only means of travel for the 65 communities of native indians who inhabit the area. Most of these people live by subsistence farming. The 20 000 Shipibo-Conibo indians live in 20 different communities around Callerias, and in addition to farming use their traditional crafts such as pottery and embroidery to earn income. Traditionally, the Shipibo-Conibo are hunter-gatherers, but now their diet consists mainly of maize, cassava flour and dried fish.

Pause for thought

Do you know where the wheat comes from to make the bread that you eat?

The Shipibo-Conibo bread-making project

Intermediate Technology Peru (ITP) has been working for about three years with the Shipibo community of Callerias, 50 miles from Pucallpa but a 5 hour boat journey. One of the main activities has been bread-baking.

The main problem is that all the bread is made in Pucallpa and transported to Callerias, which increases the price by around 30–40 per cent. Introducing a small bakery into Callerias would make bread more readily available at a cheaper price, and also provide employment for some of the native indians. Thus ITP, in collaboration with a Peruvian organization, helped to install a small bakery in Callerias. The local people were given training on how to produce bread, and they set up a small business producing a variety of breads. They now make bread from a mixture of wheat flour and cassava flour. Wheat is not available locally, so bread made solely from wheat flour would be very expensive. By mixing cassava flour, which is produced locally, with wheat flour, the community is less dependent on imported flour and the bread is cheaper.

Cassava

Cassava is an important staple crop in Africa, Asia and Latin America. The plant is a bush which grows to a height of 1–3 metres. It is a very useful crop because it will grow on poor soils and can tolerate drought. Subsistence farmers like cassava because it is grown easily from a small piece of cassava stem, and can be grown in-between other crops such as maize. The most valuable part of the plant are the starchy tubers which are formed under ground at the bottom of the stem, though none of the plant is wasted. The tubers are eaten by humans and animals; the peelings from the tubers can be added to pig and poultry feed; the green leaves are made into soup and sauces; and the stems of the plant are used for housing and building fences.

The fresh roots contain 62 per cent water, 35 per cent carbohydrate, 1 per cent protein, 1 per cent mineral matter and very little fat. Cassava is therefore a good source of carbohydrate. The small amount of protein that is present is of low quality because it is deficient in two amino acids – methionine and cysteine.

Cassava and cyanide

Great care must be taken when eating cassava because it contains cyanide. The level of cyanide varies widely (from 15 to 500 mg per kg) depending on the variety and growing conditions. Most of the cyanide is concentrated in the peel, so peeling the roots is one way of reducing the cyanide content.

R

Research activity

Find out what other staple crops are used for making flour in different parts of the world. Draw up a table which compares the nutritional properties of the flour from these different sources.

Cassava is classified into two types – sweet and bitter. Sweet cassava refers to tubers with very low levels of cyanide whilst bitter cassava has high cyanide levels. It is vital that bitter cassava is processed before it is eaten to remove the cyanide and make it safe. If bitter cassava is eaten without processing, it can cause death from cyanide poisoning, although this is rare. Sweet cassava can be eaten without any processing, and is often eaten raw.

Low levels of cyanide within the root can also be poisonous. A gradual build up of cyanide in the body can result in paralysis and goitre. Goitre results when the breakdown products of cyanide prevent the thyroid gland from obtaining iodine. It is sometimes seen in communities where cassava forms a staple part of the diet.

Preparing cassava flour

The traditional method of preparing cassava flour for bread-making in Peru is a very laborious process. The cassava roots are washed and peeled then grated to form a pulp. The pulp is squeezed to remove the excess liquid which contains some of the cyanide. It is left to stand overnight and then sieved to remove all the coarse fibres. The pulp is then roasted on a hot griddle and stirred continuously to prevent lumps forming. The dried mixture is then pounded into a flour.

To make bread, the cassava flour is mixed with wheat flour and a bread recipe followed. The bread is then baked in a wood oven.

Question

How does the preparation of cassava flour from cassava roots differ from the preparation of flour from wheat?

Research activity

1 Find out how cyanide poisons people, and what constitutes a lethal dose.

2 Find out the names of other plants which contain cyanide.

3 Find out more information about goitre; how it forms and how it can be treated.

Brand names for sweeties

Do you eat sweets?

There are really not that many types of sweets. Many are based on boiled sugar syrup, which can be made hard or soft, chewy or rubbery. We've been eating sweets for more than 100 years.

Would you chew Dulux mints, suck Samsonite gums or munch Pritt chocolates? Is it important to you that you eat Polo mints or Cadbury's chocolate or Rowntree's fruit pastilles?

Who makes sweets?

In the 1900s there were three main factories in the south-east making sweets.

Sharp's made toffee, mints and fudge, and supplied extra strong mints and toffee to the royal household. Robertson & Woodcock made boiled sweets and mints in London. It changed its name to Trebor. Can you imagine asking for a quarter of Robertson & Woodcock's marvellous menthol mints? But *Trebor* chews and *Trebor* mints sounded much better. Maynard's was based in Tottenham and made gums, jellies and pastilles. It held a royal warrant for its wine gums.

In the 1970s Trebor bought Sharp's and became Trebor-Sharp. Then in the 1980s Trebor dropped the name Sharp and bought Maynard's. Trebor now owned Sharp's and Maynard's and had established itself as a modern company with factories in several countries – people were chewing Trebor sweets all over the world! The Trebor logo was modern and stylish, and the brand names Sharp's and Maynard's were eventually abandoned – everything was Trebored!

P **Pause for thought**

Think about the sweets you buy. Do you choose branded products such as Basset's liquorice allsorts?

You know when you've been Trebored!

R **Research activity**

Investigate the sweets you eat in a week. Copy this table and chart how many and what type of sweets you eat each day in a normal week.

	Sun	Mon	Tues	Wed	Thurs	Fri	Sat
Type or brand							
Time (s)							
Amount							
Total cost							

Try to produce a graph of this information to show any patterns in your chewing!

A successful takeover

In 1989 Cadbury bought Trebor and Basset. It wanted a division of Cadbury's which just sold sugar-based confectionery, but felt that the name 'Cadbury's' made people think of chocolate. Can you imagine Cadbury's caramels, Cadbury's lemon fizzers, Cadbury's fruit drops, Cadbury's mints or Cadbury's jellies? Cadbury amalgamated the names to make Trebor-Basset and this firm was now a part of Cadbury's.

There was still the problem of what to call the sweets. Sometimes a particular brand name of a sweet is very popular, and the people who buy that sweet show brand loyalty. In other words they nearly always buy that brand in preference to any other. Because Trebor makes people think of extra strong mints, they still called the mints just that – Trebor Extra Strong Mints. Cadbury's also reinstated Sharp's Toffees and Maynard's Wine Gums, because it knew that the old-fashioned names for these products gave them an added value for many customers. Sharp's was synonymous with quality toffee and many people associate wine gums with Maynard's, so in 20 years we've gone full circle!

Questions

Describe your favourite sweet and then use attribute analysis to develop a new sweet product. Use the information in this Case Study to develop a brand name for your sweet.

▶ *Packaging indicating a quality product?*

Research activity

1 To investigate the importance of brand names try this activity. Go to your nearest sweet shop and write down as many sorts of sweets as you can see in five minutes. Write them as a list. Now try to match a brand name with each one. You may have written down a brand name as a type of sweet. If so, try to name the type of sweet. Use your lists to decide whether brand names are important.

2 As a group, buy four or more types of the same sweet. Mints are a good idea. Conduct a simple experiment to see whether, if blindfolded, people can tell what brand they are eating.

Follow the steps opposite.

1 Assemble four different mints/sweets.

2 Tell one person in your group the brand names.

3 Blindfold that person or ask them to close their eyes.

4 Give them a small piece of sweet. Ask them to name the product by brand.

5 Record your results as pie charts and use them to decide if one brand is more recognizable then the others. Your pie charts might look something like this.

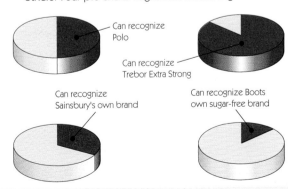

Can recognize Polo

Can recognize Trebor Extra Strong

Can recognize Sainsbury's own brand

Can recognize Boots own sugar-free brand

Bread production

Wheat

Most bread is produced from wheat flour. Wheat flour is produced by crushing wheat into a powder. To make **white** flour, the bran and germ are removed, whereas **wholemeal** flour contains all of the wheat. **Brown** flour has some of the removed bran added back to it. Which do you prefer to eat?

Wheat can be classified as being hard, soft, strong or weak. **Hard** and **soft** refer to the way the grain reacts when it is milled. In hard wheats the endosperm breaks into regular-sized pieces and separates easily from the bran. **Strong** and **weak** refer to the bread-making characteristics of the wheat. Strong wheats have a high protein content and are made into bread that has large volume, good texture and keeps well. We grow mainly soft wheat in the UK, so our bread often contains imported flour. This applies particularly to small bakers who produce premium quality bread.

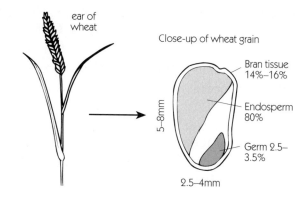

ear of wheat

Close-up of wheat grain

Bran tissue 14%–16%
Endosperm 80%
Germ 2.5–3.5%

5–8mm

2.5–4mm

I turn into strong flour

I turn into weak flour

Hard

Soft

I make good bread

Strong

I make delicate cakes and biscuits

Weak

R

Research activity

Bread has been a staple food in the UK for centuries, but we eat much less bread now than we used to. Investigate how much bread your family eats by copying out and completing the following table for each member of your family.

Eating times	Did you eat bread?	What sort?	What did you have with it?
breakfast			
mid-morning break			
lunch			
mid-afternoon break			
tea			
dinner			
supper			
other (please specify)			

Use the information from your tables to estimate how much bread (by weight) you and your family eat per week. Compare your findings with those of other class members.

Flour for bread-making

Flour is made by milling. This consists of a series of interlinked grinding and sieving operations which aim to remove as much bran as possible from the wheat grain.

Milling opens out the grain along the crease, detaches the endosperm from the bran and then reduces the particle size of the endosperm. The endosperm represents 80 per cent of the wheat kernel. Wholemeal flour by law has to contain 100 per cent of the wheat grain.

Flour for bread-making needs three important properties.

- **High gluten content**

  When wheat flour is mixed with water to form a dough, the protein absorbs water and forms a cohesive, elastic and extensible substance called **gluten**. Flour with a high protein content forms a large quantity of high quality gluten.

- **Low enzyme activity**

  When water is added to the flour there is enzyme activity, particularly alpha amylase, which breaks down starch. If this is too high it becomes difficult to cook the bread. The dough forms a sticky crumb that collapses and burns when cooked.

- **Good water absorbing properties**

  The more water that flour can absorb, the greater the volume of bread that can be produced.

  If the flour has sufficient protein content and appropriate enzyme activity, and the milling has damaged the wheat enough, then the flour will have good water absorbing properties.

Making bread in the kitchen

Bread is made from a mixture of water, flour, yeast and salt. These ingredients are mixed together to form a dough and kneaded thoroughly. The dough is then set aside for two hours, re-kneaded to improve contact between the yeast cells and the sugar, and left for a further one hour. The dough is then divided into pieces for baking, left to rest, remoulded and then left to finish rising in a humid atmosphere.

The enzymes in the yeast cause the sugar in the dough to break down giving carbon dioxide gas and ethanol. It is the carbon dioxide which causes the dough to rise. The presence of the right amount of gluten ensures that the resulting foam is stable. If there is too much gluten the dough is so stiff that it cannot rise. If there is too little gluten the dough rises but then collapses. During cooking the gluten network coagulates around the gas bubbles giving baked bread its spongy texture. Most of the ethanol evaporates during baking. Until the 1960s this was the basis for the industrial production of bread.

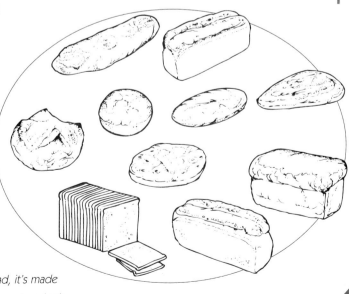

Whatever the bread, it's made from water, flour, yeast and salt

Making bread in industry

The Chorleywood process for making bread was introduced into the UK in the 1960s. Its advantage over traditional methods is that it cuts down the time needed for dough production. Also, almost any flour can be used to make bread. By using a short period of high-speed mixing, the dough can be prepared in 5 minutes compared with 3 hours using the traditional method. The amount of mechanical energy put into the dough is critical. 40 kJ/kg are needed within 2–4 minutes using a special high-speed mixer. Compared with the traditional mixing process, five times as much energy is used in one-fifth of the time. Because a large proportion of the energy used is during baking, the new process only increases energy use by about 6 per cent. After mixing, the dough is treated in the same way as in the traditional process.

The recipe for bread has to be modified in the Chorleywood process and ascorbic acid (vitamin C) needs to be added to further increase the speed of the process. However, the advantages of the new process are considerable:

- 60 per cent saving in total;
- 75 per cent less space needed;
- 75 per cent less dough is being processed at any one time;
- 4 per cent increase in yield;
- low protein flour can be used.

Question

Copy out the five advantages of the Chorleywood process. Write a sentence for each one to explain how the advantage is achieved.

Quality in the process

In food production, quality control involves both objective and subjective measurements. The most important **objective measurement** is weight. Loaves of bread are produced to a legal minimum weight. In a high volume, low profit margin product like bread, any 'over-weight' reduces the profits. So weighing is carried out throughout the process, for example:

- when the dough is divided. At this stage the dough can be remixed and redivided if necessary. If significant numbers of dough pieces are rejected, the machinery can be adjusted;
- after baking the bread is check-weighed to make sure it is not under-weight when sold.

Pause for thought

Which weighing do you think is more important, at the dough stage or at the loaf stage?

Other objective measurements can include loaf volume and crust colour. Metal detectors are also used to detect the presence of metal foreign bodies in the bread.

Taste, smell and appearance, ease of slicing and softness are examined regularly by staff who can detect small variations from the standard product. These are **subjective measurements** and depend entirely on the skill and experience of the staff.

Making minced meat

Good to eat, but hard on machines

Bachelor's Foods (now part of Vandenberg Foods) produces dried minced meat for large catering outlets such as company canteens. The mince is used to make up dishes such as shepherd's pie, lasagne and spaghetti bolognaise.

In bulk, minced meat has a consistency like bread dough and it is often called 'meat dough' by the processing companies that handle it. A machine called a meat pump is used to process the meat dough and produce minced meat. Large quantities of meat dough can be handled – the machine in this Case Study processes 800 kg per hour. The overall process is summarized in the diagram (below). As the mince is pushed out of the meat pump it is chopped into small pieces which fall onto a stainless steel conveyor belt. This takes them through a dryer before reaching the packaging stage. The dried minced meat is sent out to customers' catering outlets all over the country.

Designing a new machine

Bachelor's existing machine had become worn and corroded, as minced meat is quite abrasive and the fat in it has a corrosive effect on some metals. The machine would have taken a long time to clean and it was also very noisy. Irwin Desman Limited was therefore commissioned to design and make a meat pump to replace the one that had worn out.

P **Pause for thought**

How often do you eat minced meat in a week? Do you know how it's made and processed?

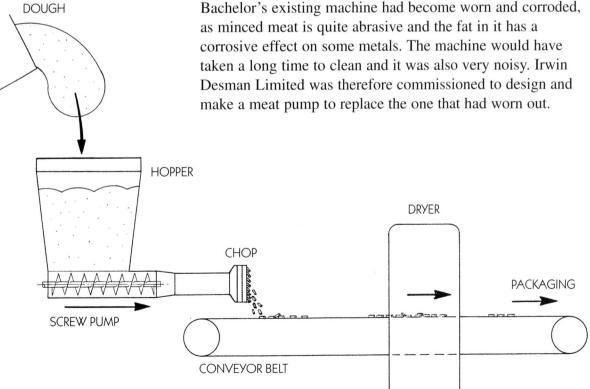

MEAT DOUGH

HOPPER

DRYER

CHOP

PACKAGING

SCREW PUMP

CONVEYOR BELT

There were several important considerations. The metal from which the pump was made had to be resistant to corrosion from the meat dough and from the regular steam-cleaning process. Stainless steel was therefore chosen. Also, all parts which might come into contact with the meat had to be completely free of cavities and recesses to ensure that the cleaning process could remove every last scrap of meat from the machine. Even a very small residue of meat left behind after cleaning could start to decay and cause contamination. The design ensured that the machine contained no cavities or 'food traps', and all surfaces were highly polished to eliminate even very small surface scratches which could harbour contamination.

The flow of meat through the pump had to be even, ensuring that the time taken for processing was similar for all the mince fed into the machine. A design which pushed only a section of meat through the pump, leaving some to spend several minutes or even hours in 'dead space' in the feed hopper, would be unacceptable due to the high risk of contamination.

After looking at the type of pump which had been used previously, the designers rejected this in favour of a large Archimedes screw. This simple mechanism would minimize the number of moving parts in contact with the meat, and would work effectively without requiring close fits and tight tolerances. To ensure an even flow of meat, it was found that the use of two Archimedes screws working alongside each other was more effective than one screw on its own.

This was especially true if the screws were driven in opposite directions (contra-rotating).

A powerful electric motor was used to drive the screw pump through a gearbox which was designed to provide speed reduction, and to drive both contra-rotating shafts. A standard electrical controller was specified by the designers, to enable the speed of the motor to be varied and thus to enable the machine operator to make fine adjustments to the pumping speed. (Where there is a choice of either designing part of a machine from scratch or using a ready-made and proven component instead, it is normally cheaper and less risky to use the proven component.)

To feed the meat into the pumping section of the machine, a gravity-fed hopper was designed using highly polished stainless steel. The new design is shown below.

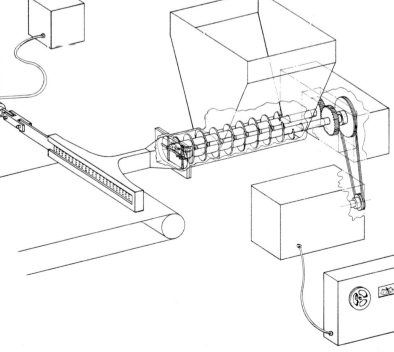

Manufacture

Making the stainless steel pumping screws for the machine presented a problem, due to their large size and in particular their long length. The problem was overcome by welding a helically formed strip of stainless steel around the outside of a stainless steel rod, rather than attempting to machine the screw from solid metal.

Operation

Having been squeezed out of the pump and through a tube, the meat dough is forced up against a plate with many holes drilled in it. This works in the same way as small, domestic mincers producing many smaller threads of extruded mince. A second metal plate moving from side to side chops the threads of mince into manageable lengths. This side to side movement is potentially the noisiest part of the process. In the old design this was operated by pneumatics and proved very noisy indeed. A much quieter means of operation was chosen by the designers, using a crank driven by a second electric motor to provide the reciprocating motion. This new mechanism is shown opposite.

Testing and commissioning

Before installing the machine in the food processing factory, Irwin Desman Limited had to fully test and prove all the working parts. A final test was conducted using the same type of meat dough which was to be processed routinely by Bachelor's Foods, with careful supervision to ensure that all the meat used for this test was disposed of afterwards. This precaution was necessary in order to comply with the strict laws governing the processing of food.

R **Research activity**

Make a small card model to show the action of the crank operating the plates.

R **Research activity**

Lots of food products are formed by extrusion in which the food material is pushed through shaped holes. Draw up a list of products that might be formed in this way, and for each one give a reason why you think it has been extruded. Check your list and your reasons with your teacher.

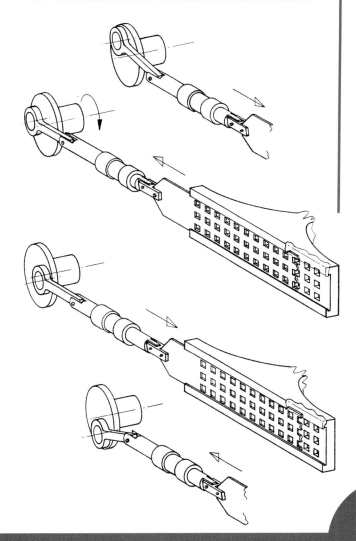

Focused case studies

Energy to make things work

The power rating of an appliance tells you how much energy is needed each second to make it work. The table on the right shows the power ratings of some appliances people use every day.

Such amounts of energy have not always been available, as the panel below shows. You can find out about the energy used to produce a loaf on page 68.

Appliance	Power rating
radio	10 watts
microwave	650 watts
electric iron	1000 watts
2-bar electric fire	2000 watts
washing maching	2500 watts
family car engine (under braking load)	37 500–45 000 watts

1000 watts = 1 kilowatt.

	Time	Power	Comment
Life without engines	prehistoric times	140 watts for a strong person	Even with simple machines and using animals, life without engines is very hard work
Wind and water power; the first engines	7th century for waterwheels in Europe after the Roman Empire, 12th century for windmills in Europe	primitive waterwheels, 300/400 watts late 18th century windmills, 2–3 kilowatts	These low-power sources are suitable for monotonous tasks like grinding corn and operating forge hammers Water power requires a suitable river and the power is only available at or very near the waterwheel Wind power requires a windy place. The power is only available at or very near the windmill and when wind is blowing
Atmospheric engines site	18th century	Newcomen's engine, 3.5 kilowatts Watt's engine, 7–8 kilowatts	Can operate wherever engine can be built and fuel transported Power only available at or near the engine

	Time	Power	Comment
True steam engines 	19th century	By the 1880s, 5000 kilowatts	Can operate wherever engine can be built and fuel transported Power only available near the engine site
Generating electricity 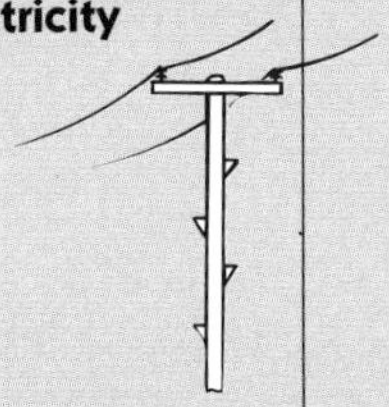	late 19th century	100 kilowatt generators used for street lighting in New York in 1882	Principles of the dynamo and electric motor understood by mid-19th century Scene set for generating and transmitting electricity which can be used to power machines that work by electric motors
Generating electricity using fossil fuel 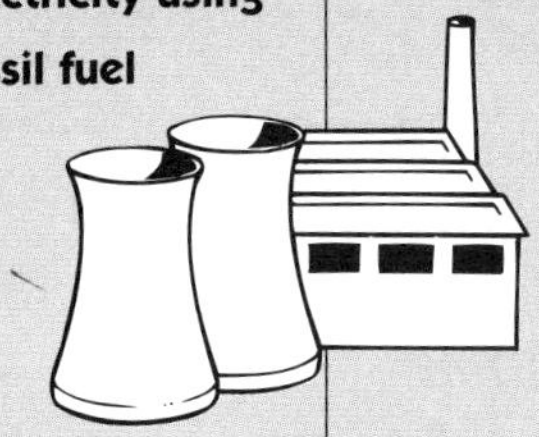	20th century	Modern power station in the UK generates 500–1000 megawatts	Contributes to acid rain unless advanced technologies used Contributes to greenhouse effect
Generating electricity using nuclear fuel 	late 20th century	Modern power station in UK generates 900 megawatts	Does not contribute to acid rain or greenhouse effect but concern over safety of power stations and disposal of radioactive waste
Generating electricity using renewable energy sources 	late 20th century	Modern windmill generates 3–4 megawatts Tidal barrier generates 240 megawatts	Does not contribute to acid rain or greenhouse effect but concern over other types of environmental impact

Focused case studies

Embedded energy

Producing a loaf

A large amount of fuel is used in the processes resulting in a loaf of bread being placed on a supermarket shelf ready for you to buy. Baking the bread uses less than one-quarter of the total fuel required, as shown in the diagram below.

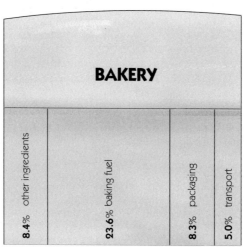

RETAIL — 8.8% shop heat & light | 12.2% transport

BAKERY — 8.4% other ingredients | 23.6% baking fuel | 8.3% packaging | 5.0% transport

MILL — 2.2% packaging | 2.4% milling fuel | 2.0% other | 1.4% transport

FARM — 0.4% other | 7.3% tractor fuel | 11.6% fertilizer

▶ *Approximately 20 000 kJ is required to produce a standard white loaf*

Bread contains 400 kJ of energy per slice; 20 slices per loaf gives 8000 kJ per loaf. So it takes two and a half times as much energy to produce a loaf of bread as you or I can get from eating it.

▶ *How much energy does this take?*

Storing a loaf at home

You can work out the energy needed to store a loaf in a freezer for a month using information from the Energy Saving Trust as follows.

Consider a freezer with energy rating E; capacity 104 litres. This will use approximately 120 000 kJ per month.

Each litre of the freezer uses 120 000 ÷ 104 kJ = 1160 kJ to keep cold each month.

A loaf takes up about 2.5 litres in volume.

So the energy cost of keeping this loaf frozen for one month is:
1160 × 2.5 kJ = 2900 kJ.

This is just over one-third of the total amount of energy available to you or me from eating the loaf.

Cool control – Manufacturing the Vienetta

Have you ever wondered just how a Vienetta is made? How do they get all those layers to fit together? It's not like making flaky pastry. How do you fold ice cream into layers? To do this the manufacturers have made use of the physical properties of ice cream.

Ice cream is soft enough to be extruded. Several tubes extrude the ice-cream onto a moving conveyor belt. By moving the tubes up and down it is possible to get a wave pattern into the ice-cream. Layers of chocolate or other fillings are sprayed onto the different layers, so the complex layer structure of the Vienetta is formed on the conveyor belt. The long, single Vienetta that is produced is then cut into portions and packaged.

The engineers who designed this production system had to take many things into account.

- The conveyor belt speed and rate of extrusion have to be just right for the layers to form properly.

- If the conveyor belt is too fast, the layers are too thin. If the conveyor belt is too slow then the layers are too thick.

- The angle of the extrusion tube to the conveyor belt is critical. Half a degree out and the layers do not form properly.

- The consistency of the ice-cream must always be the same so that it always flows from the tubes in the same way. Any variation in the flow characteristics of the ice-cream would upset the process.

- The whole thing has to be kept cold so that the ice-cream does not melt, but no so cold that it is too stiff to extrude.

Spraying of the chocolate presents similar temperature control problems. It must be warm enough to be molten for spraying but not so hot that it melts the ice-cream it is sprayed onto.

Clearly a lot of work is done on a trial-and-error basis to find the conditions necessary to form the Vienetta, and once these are found control technology is used to ensure that these optimum conditions are maintained. The involves the accurate sensing of temperature and flow rates followed by feedback of this information to a central processing unit. This in turn controls coolers and pumps that are able to make adjustments for any variations.

Identifying needs and likes

You can revise strategies for identifying needs and likes from key stage 3 by thinking about these people who visited the supermarket one Saturday morning between 9.00 and 10.30.

What won't upset my baby?

What can I afford?

I can't see anything!

I want something a bit special for the dinner party

The samosas look good. I wonder how long they'll keep?

Georgie 3-year-old boy shopping with his Dad.

Maisie 13-year-old girl buying things for her packed lunch.

Jo 28-year-old pregnant woman shopping for her family.

Jack 39-year-old man shopping for himself.

Dot 72-year-old woman shopping for two on a limited budget.

Thinking about what people might need

The people shopping at a supermarket will have different needs and likes. You can try thinking about these by using the PIES approach. PIES stands for **P**hysical, **I**ntellectual, **E**motional and **S**ocial. Each of these words describes a type of need that can be met by products that have been designed and made.

Observing people

You can find out a lot about people's needs and likes by watching them. It is important to record your observations in a way that doesn't affect what the people are doing. The picture opposite shows several different recording methods. Can you explain which ones are suitable for use in a supermarket?

Asking questions

You can find out about people's preferences by talking to them and asking questions. This is sometimes called **interviewing**. It is different from using a questionnaire as you only interview a few people. It is important to ask the right sorts of questions. To find out what each of these people want from the supermarket you would probably need to ask them different questions.

Using books and magazines

Sometimes you need to find out something by looking things up in books and magazines. Some magazines might tell you about the preferences of people using supermarkets. Where would you find these magazines? Some books might tell you about the hygiene regulations governing the chill-counter. Where would you find these books?

Image boards

You can make a collection of pictures of things that a group of people might like, places they might go, activities they might do. This is called an **image board**. An image board for Georgie would look very different from one for Maisie. Making image boards will help you understand what different people might like. It may also help you understand the style and type of products that would appeal to different people. For example, Jo and Dot may both eat fish but they will almost certainly choose very different fish-based food products.

Questions

Here is the beginning of an image board for Jo.

1 What does it tell you about her?

2 What other images could be added to give a fuller picture?

Who is Jo?

Using questionnaires

A questionnaire is a carefully designed set of questions. It is often used by businesses to find out what different groups of people like or would buy. A questionnaire will usually try to get information about the sort of person who is answering it – their occupation, how much they earn and so on. This information enables businesses to provide goods and services that people want at a price they are prepared to pay. It also shows where and when these products could be sold and how best they might be advertised. You can use a questionnaire to find out about the sorts of products people already use and what alternatives they might like.

Designing your own questionnaire

You need to be clear on what you are trying to find out. Target your questions to obtain the information you want. Avoid leading questions that suggest the answer. Avoid questions that don't discriminate, such as 'Do you like sunny days?'. Everyone always answers yes!

Sometimes you will use the questionnaire in face-to-face questioning when you record people's answers. At other times people will fill it in on their own and return it to you. In this second case it is particularly important that the meanings of the questions are clear as you won't be there to explain them.

Advice on writing questionnaire questions is given in the panel on the right.

Questions

1 Notice how newspapers and magazines use so-called questionnaires to attract the readers' interest rather than provide useful information. What sort of information do these questionnaires reveal to the readers?

Questionnaire question guide

- Use closed questions. These require a yes or no answer or give people a choice of answers.

- Make it easy to fill in the answers. Use tick boxes where possible.

- Each question should be short and simple.

- Use words people will understand.

- Write questions which only have one meaning.

- Each question should ask only one thing at a time.

- A scaled choice of answers is a good way to find out people's attitudes.

Who should I ask?

It is important that you use questionnaires with the right people. If you want to find out which food products are bought by the elderly it is important to use the questionnaire with elderly people. If you want to find out about the food eaten by toddlers then ask their parents.

What sample size should I use?

It is important to present your questionnaire to as many people as possible. This will give you a large number of responses from which you can draw reasonable conclusions. A hundred responses would be an ideal number, but this would be a huge task for one researcher. If the research is shared amongst a group of people the task becomes manageable both in terms of collecting responses and collating data. If each member of a class of 20 students took responsibility for 5 questionnaires, the sample size would be 100.

Collating the results

Once you have the returned questionnaires you will need to analyse the information. Here's how to do it.

● Draw up a summary results table or tally sheet of the possible answers to each question.

● Count how many of each possible answer you got for each question and write this in the table or on the tally sheet.

When you have done this for each question on each questionnaire the table is complete and you can begin to think about what the results mean. You will find that putting the information into a database or spreadsheet may help you collate it more quickly.

Using spreadsheets and databases

The database will organize the information so that it is easily accessible and can be displayed clearly. The database can be 'interrogated' for statistical information and thus provide a picture of user needs and likes.

Statistical information from the database can be put into a spreadsheet. The spreadsheet displays the information as rows and columns of numbers. You can analyse the information in a variety of ways and present your findings in graphical forms like pie charts and bar graphs.

Here is an example of a survey of breakfast cereal. The completed questionnaires provided information on the breakfast cereals bought by students' families.

Male ☐ Female ☐

Age 0–5 ☐ 6–10 ☐ 11–15 ☐ 16–20 ☐ 21–30 ☐ 31–40 ☐ 41–50 ☐ 51–60 ☐ 61–70 ☐ 70+ ☐

How often do you eat breakfast cereal?
every day ☐ most days ☐ 1–2 a week ☐ 1–2 a month ☐ hardly ever ☐ never ☐

When do you eat breakfast cereal?
first thing in the morning ☐ mid-morning ☐ midday ☐ mid-afternoon ☐

What do you add?
milk ☐ sugar ☐ yoghurt ☐

Total number of people surveyed = 149

Male	
Female	72
	77

What do you add?

milk	
sugar	149
yoghurt	73
	25

Design briefs

A design brief is a short statement which describes some or all of the following:

- the sort of product that is to be made and its purpose;
- who will use it;
- where it will be used;
- where it might be sold.

An **open** brief provides general guidelines and offers opportunity for a wide range of possible outcomes. A **closed** brief is more specific and detailed in its requirements.

Here are examples of open and closed briefs for two lines of interest.

Food for the elderly

Open design brief

'Design a convenience food product that will appeal to the elderly.'

Closed design brief

'Design a low-cost, long shelf-life convenience food product that will provide a main-meal dish suitable for the low-income elderly to be sold at a major supermarket chain.'

The open brief provides the designer with freedom to explore a wide range of possibilities for the food product. The closed brief provides opportunity to produce different solutions, but the nature of the product is more clearly defined so the range of possible outcomes is limited. A particular food product is required and there are only a few ways this can be achieved.

Confectionery

Open design brief

'Design a range of confectionery food products based on the theme "faraway places".'

Closed design brief

'Design a confectionery food product for the well-off young couple who enjoy entertaining. It should be suitable for the dessert of a special-occasion evening meal, be part of a series of desserts from exotic places and be sold at up-market delicatessens.'

A range of food products is possible from the open brief, including desserts, snacks and sweets. In the closed brief the type of food product, typical consumer and retail outlet are defined. This provides a more detailed picture of what is required.

Specifying the product

You will need to develop the design brief into a **performance specification**. This will provide a list of criteria against which you can assess your design as it develops.

The performance specification will always:

- describe what the product has to do. For a food product this usually means a description of its taste (flavours and textures), nutritional requirements and shelf-life;
- describe what the product should look like. For a food product you will need to think about colours, shapes and sizes;
- state any other requirements that need to be met, for example:

  what ingredients it should be made from,

  how it should be stored and prepared once purchased,

  how much it should cost to manufacture,

  possible production levels, one-off, batch or bulk production,

  legal requirements to be met in its development and sale,

  environmental considerations and requirements;

  how it should be packed for particular retail outlets.

The following panels give examples of performance specifications and products that meet their requirements.

Food product for a diabetic

What it has to do: provide the main dish of the day (no more than 400 calories).

Nutritional requirements: controlled in carbohydrate, no sugar, artificial sweeteners permitted.

Shelf-life: up to three months in the freezer.

Flavour: mainly savoury.

Texture: tender, generally soft but should require chewing, occasional crunchiness.

What it should look like: be presented as a single meal.

Other requirements:
- easy to prepare;
- suitable for microwave or conventional cooking;
- suitable for home-freezing;
- suitable for short batch production;
- relatively inexpensive – middle-range convenience food;
- ingredients can include meat or fish.

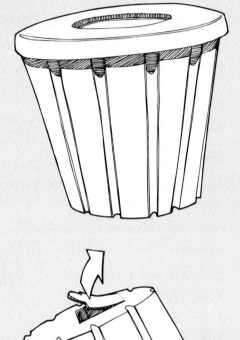

New potato products

What it should do: provide a novelty, sweet, cold, dessert dish.

Nutritional requirements: to provide a high energy boost when eaten as a snack.

Shelf-life: up to three months in the freezer.

What it should look like: a stiff, smooth jelly that keeps the shape of the container.

Other requirements:

- use potato or potato flour as the main ingredient;
- use fruit, fruit flavourings and colours as other ingredients;
- suitable for home-freezing;
- easy-release packaging for dessert or eat from the package as a snack;
- should appeal to the novelty dessert/snack market for children aged 5–12.

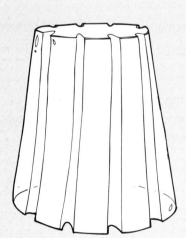

Generating design ideas

Brainstorming

You probably did some brainstorming at key stage 3. Here is a reminder.

Brainstorming is:

- a process for getting ideas out of your head!
- a process for getting ideas you didn't know you had!
- a process which uses questions and associations and links ideas to actions;
- a process you can do on your own, but it is usually better in a group.

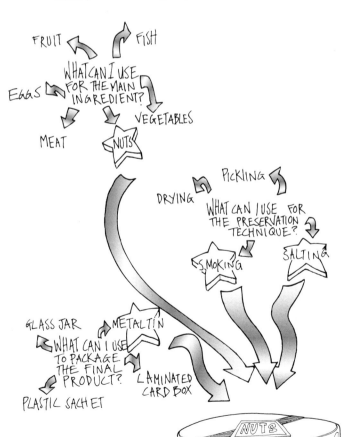

Brainstorming an idea can help you to identify a wider range of options for your designing and making and to work out how best to develop these ideas.

How to brainstorm

- First state the problem or need.
- Record every idea suggested as words, phrases or pictures.
- Produce as many ideas as possible.
- Don't make judgements until the brainstorming pattern is complete.
- Allow enough time for new and diverse ideas to emerge, but agree a time limit so that ideas remain fresh.
- Sort out ideas by considering which are unrealistic, inappropriate and unachievable and removing them. What is left will give you a focus for action.

What can I use for this?

By asking the question 'What can I use for this?' you can identify design options. You can give each possibility a yes/no verdict based on specific criteria – availability, cost, effectiveness and feasibility. You can refine the remaining options using similar criteria until you are left with a 'best' solution. Here is an example, to do with developing a preserved food product.

The designer asked, 'What can I use for this?' for each of three areas as shown opposite.

In the end the designer opted for a mix of smoked and salted nuts packed in a decorative metal tin (with a pull-off lid) which could be used as a bowl.

4

What can I use this for?

This is the sort of brainstorming you use when you have a product and want to find out if you can change its image and sell it to a different and larger consumer group. A good example of this is the advertising campaign for the soft drink Lucozade.

Initially Lucozade was a product bought for people, both children and adults, who were recovering from illness. Now Lucozade is seen as a drink for fit, active people who play sports. By asking the question 'What can I use this for?' the manufacturers of Lucozade were able to completely change the consumer group that bought their product.

The chart below shows the results of the brainstorm.

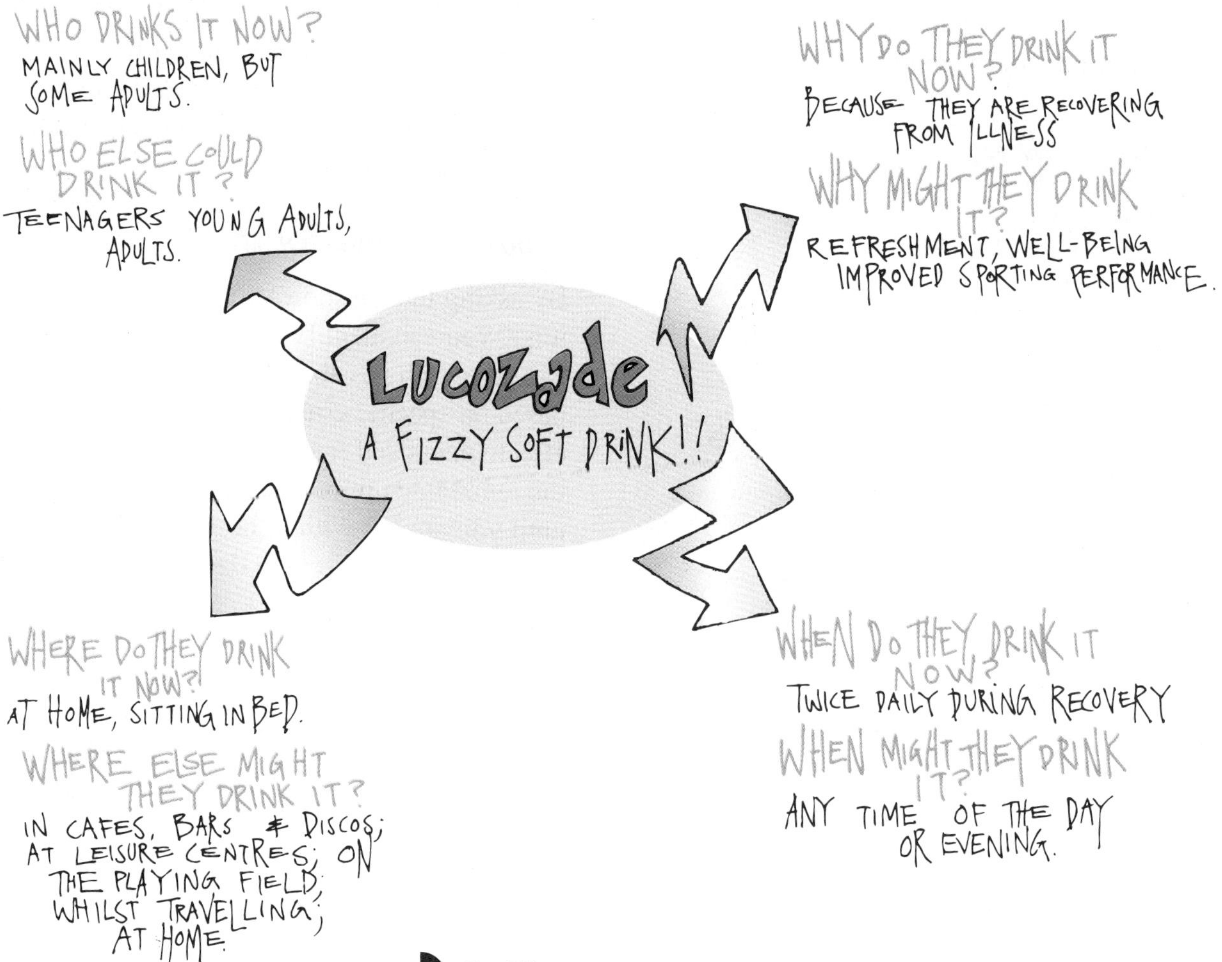

WHO DRINKS IT NOW?
MAINLY CHILDREN, BUT SOME ADULTS.

WHO ELSE COULD DRINK IT?
TEENAGERS, YOUNG ADULTS, ADULTS.

WHY DO THEY DRINK IT NOW?
BECAUSE THEY ARE RECOVERING FROM ILLNESS

WHY MIGHT THEY DRINK IT?
REFRESHMENT, WELL-BEING, IMPROVED SPORTING PERFORMANCE.

Lucozade
A FIZZY SOFT DRINK!!

WHERE DO THEY DRINK IT NOW?!
AT HOME, SITTING IN BED.

WHERE ELSE MIGHT THEY DRINK IT?
IN CAFES, BARS & DISCOS; AT LEISURE CENTRES; ON THE PLAYING FIELD; WHILST TRAVELLING; AT HOME.

WHEN DO THEY DRINK IT NOW?
TWICE DAILY DURING RECOVERY

WHEN MIGHT THEY DRINK IT?
ANY TIME OF THE DAY OR EVENING.

The 'What can I use Lucozade for?' brainstorm

Observational drawing

You can use observational drawing to give you a reference for what things look like and to help you get ideas. Often the shape and form of a food product, or the decoration on a food product, is based on a natural form – a flower, a leaf, an animal. However, food materials often change their shape and size during processing, so very precise and detailed outlines are often impractical. In such cases it is often more important for the resemblance to be just recognizable rather than precise.

The shape or form that you draw will be a simplification of the one that you observe. In order to achieve this you may need to do a realistic drawing first. Here are some examples of simplified forms that have been useful in designing food products.

Strategies – generating ideas

Attribute analysis

You may have used attribute analysis at key stage 3. Designers and engineers use it to help them produce new designs for familiar products.

Here is an attribute analysis table for the snack biscuit KitKat. The headings describe attributes which will affect the final design.

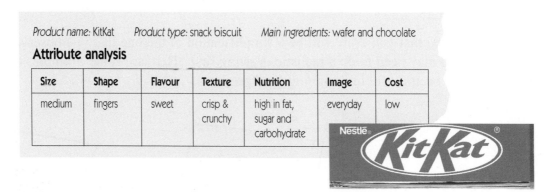

Product name: KitKat   *Product type:* snack biscuit   *Main ingredients:* wafer and chocolate

Attribute analysis

Size	Shape	Flavour	Texture	Nutrition	Image	Cost
medium	fingers	sweet	crisp & crunchy	high in fat, sugar and carbohydrate	everyday	low

You can develop the table by listing possible attributes in each of the columns, as shown below. Then you can read across the columns and combine different words from each column to create new designs. Some combinations will be totally inappropriate, while others will offer viable design ideas. Be prepared to be surprised – a medium-sized sphere that is sweet, sickly, creamy, gooey and high in fat and sugar, has a sleazy image and is low cost sounds terrible, until you think of a chocolate cream egg!

Attribute analysis development – Example 1

Size	Shape	Flavour	Texture	Nutrition	Image	Cost
small	fingers	sweet	soft	**fat**	everyday	low
medium	circle	sour	firm	sugar	**special**	medium
large	oval	salty	hard	**salt**	modern	**high**
	rectangle	bitter	dry	fibre	**traditional**	
	square	**savoury**	moist	**carbohydrate**	healthy	
	triangle	spicy	**crumbly**	vitamins	luxury	
	sphere	sickly	**crisp**	minerals	sleazy	
	thin	herbal	crunchy		hi-tech	
	thick	fishy	brittle		green	
	wide	meaty	thin			
	narrow	fruity	creamy			
	animal		sticky			
	plant		tough			
			tender			
			chewy			
			rubbery			
			gritty			
			greasy			
			gooey			
			slimy			

Once you have a list of attributes that describe an interesting and possible product, you can begin to think about the main ingredients that might be needed and develop a recipe for a prototype. Two examples are shown here.

Example 1 gives us expensive, leaf-shaped, cheese-flavoured biscuits, to be served with drinks before a meal. Example 2 gives us medium-cost, endangered species-shaped fruit biscuits for a child's school lunch.

Attribute analysis development – Example 2

Size	Shape	Flavour	Texture	Nutrition	Image	Cost
small	fingers	sweet	soft	fat	everyday	low
medium	circle	sour	firm	**sugar**	special	**medium**
large	oval	salty	hard	salt	modern	high
	rectangle	bitter	dry	**fibre**	traditional	
	square	savoury	**moist**	carbohydrate	healthy	
	triangle	spicy	**crumbly**	vitamins	luxury	
	sphere	sickly	**crisp**	minerals	sleazy	
	thin	herbal	crunchy		hi-tech	
	thick	fishy	brittle		**green**	
	wide	meaty	thin			
	narrow	**fruity**	creamy			
	animal		sticky			
	plant		tough			
				tender		
				chewy		
				rubbery		
				gritty		
				greasy		
				gooey		
				slimy		

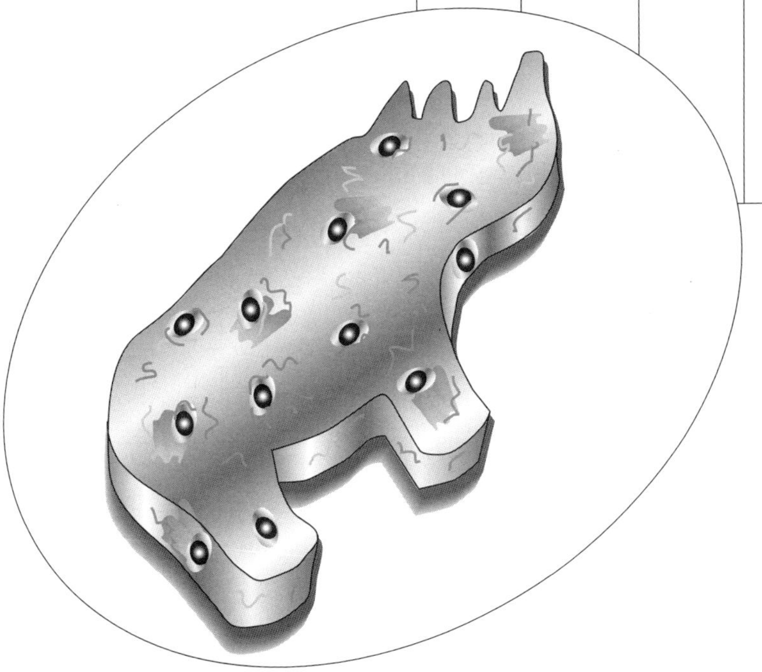

Defining and refining food product ideas

It is difficult to imagine what your food product will look like or how it will work without having something to look at, think about and test. To begin with you can define your ideas using bullet-point notes and some annotated sketches. Defining your ideas is important because it helps you:

- clarify and develop your design ideas;
- evaluate your design ideas;
- share your design ideas with others.

Once you have these initial ideas it is important to produce a prototype food product quickly so that you can refine it by testing and modifying. Here is an example of the defining and refining of a confectionery food product based on fudge.

1 Talking it through

Talking with other people about what you want to do will help you clarify your design ideas.

By talking about food materials for confectionery, Darren identified fudge as a possibility.

2 Bullet-point notes

Darren noted down five reasons why fudge would be a good choice.

3 Quick annotated sketching

He found a recipe for fudge and described it by means of an annotated sketch.

4 Making and testing a prototype

He tried out the fudge recipe and carried out some simple tasting tests himself.

- Was it sweet enough or too sweet?
- Was it too sickly?
- Was it firm enough or too soft?
- Was it dry enough or too gooey?

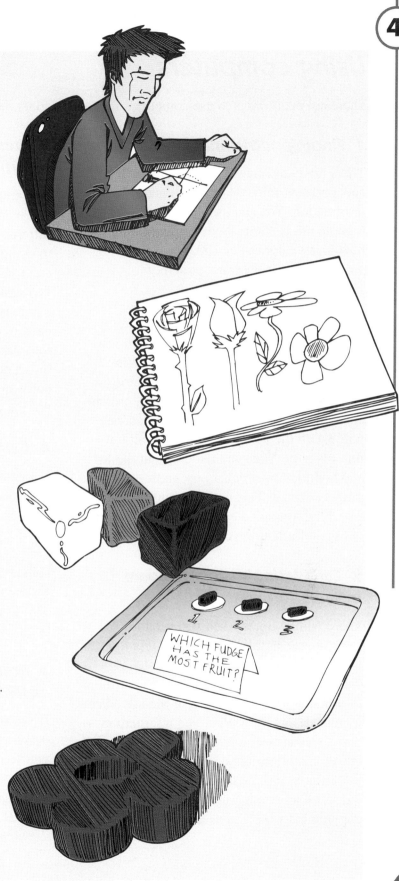

5 Refining the taste with attribute profiles

From this he decided on the following targets:

- less sweet;
- a little more moist but not gooey.

He used a series of tastings to compare the modified recipes with the original product and with each other until he got the profile he wanted.

6 Refining the shape and form by observational drawing

To get the simple flower shapes, he made observational drawings leading to simplified versions he could cut out easily.

7 Refining the finish by trialing decoration techniques

Darren produced three different versions – plain, white and dark chocolate. He found that most people preferred the plain version for both taste and appearance.

8 Controlling the cost by difference testing

Darren was able to show that he could reduce the amount of chopped dried fruit by half before anyone noticed the difference.

9 The final fudge

It looks good, tastes right and doesn't cost too much to make.

Using computers

There are many ways to use computers for food product design. Here are some examples.

1 Finding nutritional information

There are many databases available which contain large amounts of nutritional information. You can use these databases to look up information about particular foods – how many calories per 100 g, and the amounts of carbohydrate, protein, fats, vitamins and minerals present.

On some databases you can 'interrogate' the information and ask questions that will lead you to the food materials you are looking for. You provide information such as a calorific value between certain limits, and fat, protein and carbohydrate content, and the database will list all the food materials that fall into this category. You can then print out the list and highlight materials to try out in your food product design. This is much quicker than searching through a book of data and copying out the information you want.

2 Calculating with nutritional information

There will be times when you need to calculate the nutritional qualities of a food product design. By using a nutritional database you will be able to list the nutritional information describing each of the ingredients in your design. If you put this information into a spreadsheet it will calculate the overall nutritional information for your product and present it as a printed table. This is much quicker than looking it up in a book and copying out what you need.

3 Presenting and comparing nutritional information

It is much easier to compare the information if it is in visual form. If you have several different food product designs and you want to compare their nutritional information you can use the spreadsheet information obtained in 2 above to produce a bar chart or pie chart summarizing the nutritional information for each of your designs. You can then print out the charts as they stand or incorporate them into a document by using desk-top publishing software. This is much quicker than drawing out the charts by hand.

4 Calculating costings

Sometimes you will need to calculate the cost of a food product design. By using an ingredient price database you will be able to list the prices of all of the ingredients in your design. If you put this information into a spreadsheet you can calculate the overall cost for your product and present it as a table. This is much quicker than looking it up in a book and copying out what you need.

5 Presenting and comparing costings

If you have several different food product designs and you want to compare their cost you can use the spreadsheet information obtained in 4 above to produce a bar chart or pie chart summarizing the cost for each of your designs. This is much quicker than drawing out the charts by hand.

Initial drawing

Finished plain muffin

Banana icing & cherry

Chocolate covered

Icing & 'hundreds & thousands'

Whipped cream & fruit

Possible muffins finished by Katie Parker using Adobe Illustrator

6 Presenting variations on food product appearance

There will be times when you are not sure what finish to use on your food product design. Should the muffins be iced or left plain? If they are iced, which colour? Maybe they could be iced on just a small part of the muffin. Could chocolate be used?

It would take a long time to test out each idea. If you draw a picture of the biscuit on your computer (or scan it in) you can generate lots of copies of the image and finish each one in a slightly different way. In this way you can see what many different finishes would look like without making any of them. You can then print out a picture of each different product, which is much quicker than drawing the different finishes. Of course the print-out only tells you about the appearance of the products, not their taste!

Applying science

Understanding colloids

Colloids are important in food products. Butter, milk, ice-cream, jelly, salad cream, sauces, bread and cake are all colloids of one sort or another. A colloid is a mixture of two things that don't normally mix. Take Aero chocolate, for example. Normally air and chocolate don't mix, but if you whisk air into molten chocolate and then cool the chocolate before the air has had time to separate out you are left with a colloid – a solid foam of chocolate and air. If you change the size of the air bubbles you change the texture of the chocolate. This is why Wispa and Aero chocolate taste different.

Fruit jellies are made from a protein called gelatine. The solid, rubbery gelatine is dissolved in warm water. This is not a true solution – it is called a **sol**. If you were to shine a light through the warm liquid you would see the path of the light beam. This is because the gelatine molecules are so large.

As the gelatine in water sol cools, the gelatine molecules form a continuous network throughout the liquid. A **gel** is formed in which droplets of water are trapped in the gelatine. This is what happens when the jelly sets. If you use too much water, the gelatine molecules are too far apart to form the network, and the jelly doesn't set.

Mayonnaise is a colloid in which droplets of vegetable oil are held in suspension in vinegar (a solution of acetic acid in water). Liquid-in-liquid colloids like this are called **emulsions**. Oil and vinegar don't mix, and if you try to make an emulsion by shaking them together, it seems to work at first but then after you stop shaking the two liquids separate out.

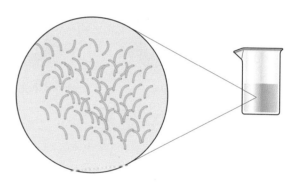

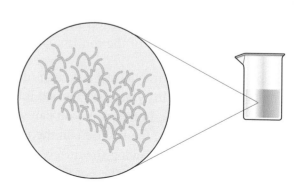

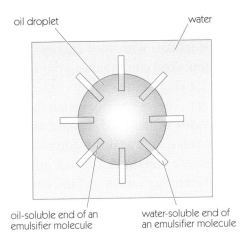

oil droplet

water

oil-soluble end of an emulsifier molecule

water-soluble end of an emulsifier molecule

Ingredients:

Vegetable oil, Hydrogenated vegetable oil, Reconstituted whey powder, Salt, Emulsifiers, E322, E471, Citric and Lactic Acids, Flavouring, Colour, E160(a), Vitamins A and D.

To form a stable emulsion you need an **emulsifying agent**. In mayonnaise, it is the presence of egg yolk, which contains the emulsifying agent lecithin, that prevents the oil and vinegar from separating.

Emulsifiers work like this. The molecules of the emulsifier have the special property that one end is attracted to water while the other end is attracted to oil. In mayonnaise, emulsifier molecules end up with one end buried in an oil droplet and the other end buried in the surrounding vinegar. This keeps the small droplets of oil in suspension, as shown, opposite.

Food manufacturers usually use lecithin made from soya bean oil because it is cheaper. Another emulsifier often used by food manufacturers is glycerol monostearate (GMS). This is a compound formed naturally in the body when you digest fats. It can be made synthetically from glycerol and stearic acid. Emulsifiers like these are called **additives** and those used to make emulsions have E numbers ranging from E322 to E494. These are listed on food product labels, as shown opposite.

Stabilizers also help to make food emulsions. They increase the thickness of the mixture which stops the oil droplets coming together. Natural polymers are used, including starch. Other carbohydrates with long-chain molecules are used too, including agar (E406) and carrageen (E407) which is extracted from seaweeds. Gelatine may be used, or natural gums such as locust bean gum (E410) or gum tragacanth (E413). Many of the emulsifiers and stabilizers added to food come from natural sources.

Strategies – applying science

Understanding the nutrition-respiration relationship

When food materials are digested they are broken down into smaller and smaller molecules until they can pass through the gut wall and into the bloodstream. These small food molecules are then transported throughout the body so that every cell receives food. The way each cell makes use of these food molecules is called **respiration**.

Take glucose as an example. The enzymes in each cell enable glucose to react with the oxygen that is transported around the body in the bloodstream. In this reaction the glucose combines with the oxygen to form carbon dioxide and water. These waste products are transported by the bloodstream to parts of the body where they can be excreted. The energy that was held by the glucose is released and trapped in chemicals in the cell. It can be used by the cell for a variety of life processes, such as growth, maintenance and repair. Imagine the reaction between glucose and oxygen as being like the burning of glucose, then in the cell most of the energy that would be released as heat is trapped in the cell to do useful work. The cells in our body carry out the reaction of glucose with oxygen at body temperature.

Scientists can work out the energy in the foods we eat by burning them and measuring the heat energy released. This is the same amount as is 'captured' by the body during respiration. If you take in just enough food to meet your energy requirements your weight will stay constant. If you take in too much then the body stores this excess as fatty deposits. If food becomes short the body can draw on these reserves. This is why people get thinner when they starve.

When trying to keep your weight constant it is important to match your energy intake (and hence food intake) with your energy requirements. You can monitor your energy intake by looking at the energy content of the food you eat. This is usually called the **calorific value** of the food. People sometimes talk about being on a 'calorie-controlled diet'. In a diet to lose weight there is an imbalance between the energy intake and the energy expenditure – the food provides less energy than is used. Here is a list of the calorific values of typical foods. Note that the information is given in two forms: as energy per 100 g and energy per typical portion.

Food	Energy content				
	per 100 g			per portion	
	in cals	in joules	portion size	in cals	in joules
Fish: cod in batter fried in oil	199	834	150 g	299	1251
Meat: pork chop, loin, grilled	226	945	125 g	283	1181
Poultry: roast chicken (meat only)	148	621	100 g	148	621
Cheese: cheddar	412	1708	75 g	309	1281
Eggs: boiled	147	612	1 egg (60 g)	88	367
Bread: wholemeal	215	914	2 slices (70 g)	151	640
Margarine	739	3039	10 g for 2 slices	74	304
Low-fat spread	390	1605	10 g for 2 slices	39	161
Crisps	546	2275	1 × 25 g pkt	137	569
Yoghurt: low fat, fruit	90	382	125 g	113	478
Tomato, raw	17	73	1	13	55
Apple, raw	47	199	1 (75 g)	59	149

The information in the table above has been obtained by scientists using food calorimeters. These burn the foods and measure the heat energy released.

Systems thinking

During your key stage 3 work you may have been introduced to systems thinking. You can use this to help you understand the way food products are produced. When a designer is beginning to design a food production system he or she only needs to consider what goes into the system and what comes out. They do not need to worry just yet about what happens inside the system. All the things that go into the system are called **inputs** and all those that come out are called **outputs**. For a fast-food production system the designer might identify the inputs and outputs shown below.

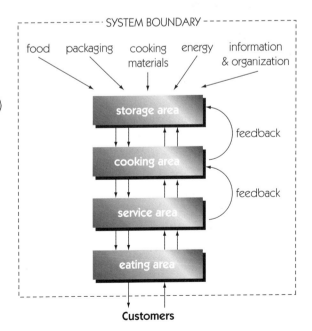

▶ Some inputs and outputs of a fast-food service

The designer will then break down the system into subsystems and see how the inputs and outputs need to be arranged. A systems diagram showing these inputs and outputs is shown opposite.

You should note the following.

- It doesn't look like a fast-food service but it does help you understand how one works.

- The output of one subsystem becomes the input of another.

- There is feedback of information from one subsystem to another. This allows the system to be controlled. For example, if the number of people buying food increases there is feedback from the serving area to the cooking area telling the cooking area to produce more food. If the number of people buying food decreases there is feedback telling the cooking area to produce less food. Systems with this type of feedback are called **closed-loop systems**.

- The designer has drawn the system boundary to include the eating area of the fast-food service but not its immediate surroundings. As many customers will take out the food there may be litter problems. To address this issue he or she could redraw the boundary to include the immediate surroundings and provide a subsystem to deal with discarded packaging.

```
┌ ─ ─ ─ SYSTEM BOUNDARY ─ ─ ─ ─ ─ ┐

food   packaging   cooking   energy   information
                   materials          & organization

          ┌──────────────────┐
          │   storage area   │
          └──────────────────┘          feedback
          ┌──────────────────┐
          │   cooking area   │
          └──────────────────┘
          ┌──────────────────┐          feedback
          │   service area   │
          └──────────────────┘
          ┌──────────────────┐
          │   eating area    │
          └──────────────────┘
└ ─ ─ ─ ─ ─ ─ ─ ─ ─ ─ ─ ─ ─ ─ ─ ─ ┘
                Customers
```

▶ Systems diagram of a fast-food service

User and operator interfaces

The parts of a system used by people are called **user interfaces**. For the customers of the fast-food service the user interface is the counter where they place their orders. In most fast-food outlets this interface is a **human interface**, but **machine interfaces** are becoming increasingly common. These include snack and soft drink vending machines, banking machines and train ticket machines. Human interfaces are more friendly and can explain things and answer queries. However, they do require special training and are not usually available 24 hours a day.

A machine interface has the advantage of always being available, but it can appear unfriendly and difficult to use. Machine interfaces should be designed to be self explanatory and user friendly.

◨ *A human user interface using a machine operator interface*

The parts of a system operated by the people who play a part in running and controlling the system are called **operator interfaces**. They are usually more complicated than user interfaces because operators need more information and have to be able to do more things than users.

Operators are therefore usually trained to operate the system while users are not. The operator must be able to put information into the system through easy-to-use controls – the operator interface should be as easy to use as possible. The keypad used by the servers at a fast-food outlet is a good example of an operator interface.

A closer look at feedback and control

The chip-fryer in the cooking area and the freezer in the storage area provide examples of feedback and control. It is important that the fat in the fryer does not overheat causing burned chips or, even worse, a fire. It is important that the freezer stays below a certain temperature otherwise the food will spoil and become dangerous to eat. These systems diagrams show how temperature sensors are used to provide the feedback needed for temperature control.

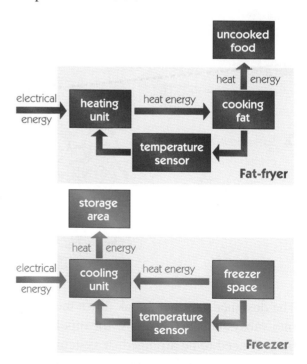

◨ *Temperature control system for fat-fryer and a freezer*

Planning

Flow charts and Gantt charts

You can use flow charts and Gantt charts to help you plan your way through a Capability Task. In year 11 you may spend as much as two whole terms on a single Capability Task as part of your GCSE assessment. It will be important to ensure that holidays, sports' days, etc. don't spoil your plans. You can use the headings in the flow chart shown opposite to get the order of the task right. Once you have the order right you can use a Gantt chart to think about how long each part should take and to make sure that you get the task done on time. A Gantt chart will give you an overview of the whole task, showing both what needs to be done and when it should be done.

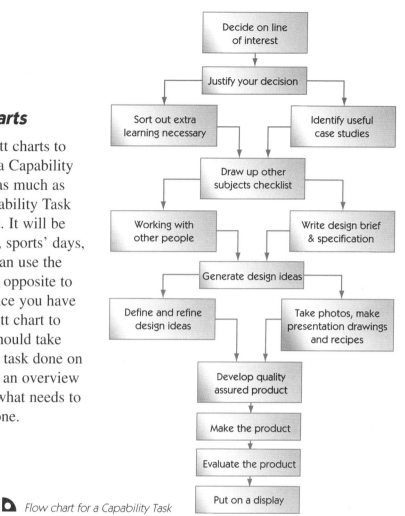

Flow chart for a Capability Task

Week 1	Week 2	Week 3	Week 4	Week 5	Week 6	Week 7	Week 8	Week 9	Week 10	Week 11	Week 12
Decide line of interest Justify decision Extra learning Case studies											
		Other subjects Other people Brief & Spec									
		Generating design ideas									
			Define and refine design ideas Take photos, make presentation drawings and recipes								
								Developing quality assured production			
									Final production		
										Evaluating the product	
										Display	
11 weeks to go	10 weeks to go	9 weeks to go	8 weeks to go	7 weeks to go	6 weeks to go	5 weeks to go	4 weeks to go	3 weeks to go	2 weeks to go	1 week to go	

Evaluating

User trip

One of the simplest ways to evaluate a product is to take a user trip. This involves using the product and asking a few basic questions.

- Is it easy or convenient to use?
- Does it do what it is supposed to do?
- Do I like it?
- Would I want to own it or continue to use it?

The manager of an ice-cream parlour in a multi-screen cinema was very keen to introduce some new flavours as a way of boosting trade. He arranged for some free sample-tasting sessions before the start of the main evening performances. The thoughts of some customers who took the user trip are shown opposite.

Winners and losers

The outcomes of design and technology will provide benefits for some and disadvantages for others. Designing and making a product will affect lots of people directly and indirectly.

A large estate has a small shopping centre in its main street – a small supermarket, post office, chemists, newsagents, and a fish and chip shop. All these businesses are quite successful. Now a Chinese takeaway food shop has opened just 100 metres from the fish and chip shop. The fish and chip shop opens at lunchtimes and tea-times twice a week; the Chinese takeaway will open lunchtimes and evenings six days a week. This Winners and Losers Chart identifies some of those people directly and indirectly affected by the availability of new and different food products. Who do you think are winners and losers? Who else will be affected?

SRT7
SRT8

Ranking tests

This type of test will help you evaluate the strength of a particular quality of the food. It is good for deciding on flavour, colour and texture. Here is an example.

Which dried fruit gives the sweetest tasting muesli?

Make three batches of muesli each with the same amount of a different dried fruit.

Set up your tasting panel like this:

Your results might look like this:

Taster A		Taster B		Taster C		Taster D	
1	▲	1	▲	1	●	1	●
2	●	2	●	2	▲	2	▲
3	■	3	■	3	■	3	■

	1	2	3
●	✓✓✓	✓	
▲	✓	✓✓✓	
■			✓✓✓✓

Turn the results into a chart like this

The ticks tell you the **rank order**. From this small sample, muesli ● is thought to be the most sweet.

Note: the ranking test does not tell you whether the tasting panel preferred one muesli to another. For that you need a preference test.

Difference tests

This type of test is useful for finding out whether people can tell the difference between slightly different food products. Here is an example.

Can people tell the difference between an ice-cream made with sugar and one made with artificial sweetener?

Make up two recipes and prepare three samples of food labelled with symbols:

- sample ▲ made with sugar;
- sample ■ made with artificial sweetener;
- sample ● made with artificial sweetener.

Samples ■ and ● are identical.

Give each taster a sheet like the one shown.

You then count up the number who could tell the difference.

It is probable that the correct answer chosen by chance is 33.3 per cent or one-third. If more than one-third of your tasters choose sample ▲ as being different, you need to make more changes. If fewer than one-third choose sample ▲ as being different then your recipe is acceptable. This is often called a **triangle test**.

Strategies – evaluating

Preference tests

This sort of test is used to find out how much a person likes or dislikes a food. Use a five-point scale of descriptive words or faces (for young children) to help people describe how much they like the product. Here is an example.

How much do you like the chocolates?

Set up a tasting panel like this:

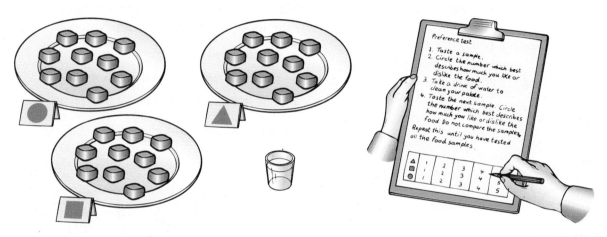

With ten tasters your results might look like this:

▲	5	4	5	4	4	2	4	3	5	3
●	3	3	5	4	2	1	3	4	2	5
■	1	1	1	3	2	3	1	2	3	2

Turn the results into a chart like this

	Total score	Average score	Conclusion
▲	39	39/10 = 3.9	disliked moderately
■	32	32/10 = 3.2	neither liked nor disliked
●	19	19/10 = 1.9	liked moderately

You can draw a conclusion about how much the tasting panel liked each sample as shown in the last column of the table. This type of test is called a **hedonic ranking** test.

Evaluation by attribute profile

This method allows you to describe a product in terms of tasters' responses to a range of attributes. You can present the description visually as an **attribute profile**. Here is an example showing the response of tasters to the attributes of a bacon and avocado sandwich. Tasters are asked to give a score for each of four attributes. The average scores are shown here:

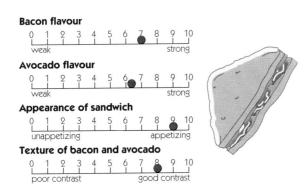

▶ Average attribute scores for brown bread, bacon and avocado sandwich

The results are displayed as an attribute profile like this:

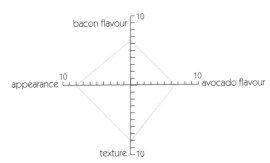

▶ Attribute profile for brown bread, bacon and avocado sandwich

You can use this profile to develop different products with similar or improved profiles. To do this, modify these features and test the tasters' responses to the new product, and present the results as an attribute profile. By comparing the two profiles you can decide whether the modification has improved the product as far as the tasters are concerned. You can test a range of modifications in this way, as shown here.

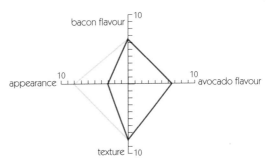

▶ Attribute profile for white bread, bacon and avocado sandwich compared with profile for brown bread, bacon and avocado sandwich

When white bread is used instead of brown, the low score for appearance and the resulting change in the shape of the profile indicates that the product is less appealing. It is therefore not worth making this change.

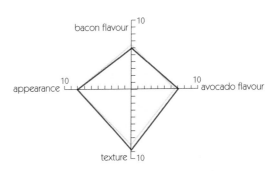

▶ Attribute profile for brown bread, bacon and avocado sandwich with reduced bacon compared with profile for brown bread, bacon and avocado sandwich

By reducing the amount of bacon in the sandwich the cost can be reduced. Tasters' responses gave an attribute profile almost identical in shape to the original, so it is worth making this change.

Performance testing

Evaluating a product will involve comparing how well it works with its performance specification. This is called performance testing. Here is the specification for a very basic pasta sauce:

- flavour – spicy, hot, tomato with garlic;
- texture – smooth and viscous, sticking to and coating the pasta;
- colour – intense, bright red;
- ingredients should be suitable for vegetarians;
- suitable for microwave and conventional cooking;
- shelf-life of 3 months in unopened bottle, eat within 5 days of opening, store in refrigerator after opening;
- low cost;
- packaged to appeal to young people on low incomes.

To carry out a performance test you would need to do the following.

1   Check the flavour – is it really spicy, hot, tomato with garlic? You can carry out a taste test yourself or use a tasting panel.

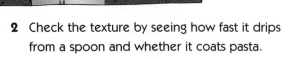

2   Check the texture by seeing how fast it drips from a spoon and whether it coats pasta.

3   Check the colour either yourself or by asking others to assess the colour.

4   Check the ingredients, including any cooking oil used.

5   Cook the sauce both conventionally (heating in a saucepan) and in a microwave oven. Compare the results – they should be identical.

6   It is tricky to test for shelf-life in school, and you should not try taste tests after storage. You can check for signs of deterioration by looking and smelling, but you must take strict hygiene precautions.

7   Double the cost of the ingredients to take into account the cost of manufacturing and distribution. Compare this figure with the price of a similar shop-bought product. It should be less if the product is to be low cost.

8   Compare your packaging suggestions against that used for similar products on sale in the local supermarket. To be successful your packaging should be similar so that the type of product and the price range are easily identifiable, yet have some distinguishing features which make it stand out.

Is it appropriate?

Appropriate technology is suitable technology. You can use these questions to find out if a product or technology is appropriate.

- Does it suit the needs of the people who use it?
- Does it use local materials?
- Does it use local means of production?
- Is it too expensive?
- Does it generate income?
- Does it increase self-reliance?
- Does it use renewable sources of energy?
- Is it culturally acceptable?
- Is it environmentally friendly?
- Is it controlled by users?

It is unlikely that any product or technology will score highly against all these questions. Many will seem appropriate in one context and inappropriate in another. Here is a situation in which the availability of food products has an effect on the members of a family.

Emma is 14 years old. She likes to have a snack before she starts her homework. She can achieve this in several ways.

1 Eat a bag of chips on the way home from school.

2 Get herself some toast and jam when she gets in from school.

3 Toast a pop tart when she gets in from school.

Each of these situations uses a different food product. There are advantages and disadvantages for each one. Which do you think is the most appropriate food product for Emma? Will the answer always be the same whatever the situation?

Emma's parents both work and don't get in until 6.30 p.m. When possible they like to eat an evening meal with their children – Emma aged 14, Sally aged 16, Nat aged 19. They can achieve this in several ways.

1 Ask Emma, Sally and Nat to get a meal ready for 6.30.

2 Ask Emma, Sally and Nat to prepare the ingredients for a meal that their parents cook when they get in at 6.30.

3 Choose something they can prepare and cook quickly when they get in.

4 Use ready-prepared convenience food that only requires heating.

5 Buy everyone some hot food on the way home.

Which food products would you use for each possibility? How appropriate is the use of these food products? Which is the best way for the family to eat together? Will the answer always be the same whatever the situation?

Remember: whether a product or technology is appropriate will depend on the situation in which it is used.

Strategies Chooser Chart

This Chooser Chart gives you information about strategies:

- when to use a strategy in a Capability Task;
- how long the strategy will take;
- how complex it is;
- whether it involves other people.

Key to icons:

When: beginning – middle – end

Time: short – long

Complexity: simple to complex

Other people: one other to many

Strategy	Comments
Identifying needs and likes	
PIES	
observing people	
asking questions	
using books and magazines	
image boards	
questionnaires	
Design briefs	
Specifications	
Generating design ideas	
brainstorming	
attribute analysis	
observational drawing	
investigative drawing	
Defining ideas (notes and sketches)	
Prototyping	
Refining ideas (through sensory testing)	
Applying science	
Using computers	
Systems thinking	
Planning	
Evaluating	
ranking test	
difference test	
preference test	
user trip	
winners and losers	
attribute profile	
performance specification	
appropriateness	

Communicating your design proposals

Who to?

Design proposals for new or improved food products can only be turned into saleable items if the design team communicates its proposals effectively to clients, manufacturers and users. **Clients** are often large supermarket chains and the designers may be an in-house team. The users are those who buy and use the product (the **consumers**).

To begin with, a small design team will develop a range of ideas for new products. Weak or impractical ideas will be discarded until the team has a workable design idea. The product will be developed to prototype stage and then refined by a series of tastings and modifications until the design team are satisfied that the product will be successful in the market. It is at this point that the design team must convince the client that its product can be produced in bulk and sold at a profit. If the regional trials are successful then the product can be launched nationally, selling through supermarkets across the country. The manufacturers will vary in size from large concerns that can produce many thousands of products per day, to small businesses that produce only a few hundred. It is the response of the consumer to the product that governs its success or failure.

There are three important areas of communication in this process.

1 Communicating with the client about the nature of the proposed food product. If the client is not convinced that the product will be successful then it will not go into production.

2 Communicating with the manufacturer about the means of producing the product. If this communication is poor then the products manufactured will be of low or variable quality and will not sell well.

3 Communicating with the customer through the packaging and advertising of the product. If this is unsuccessful the product will not sell.

Each of these requires special communication techniques which are described in the rest of this unit.

◗ Good communication was needed for these products to be on sale in a supermarket

Presenting the product to the client

What it looks like

The 'just served' look is difficult to achieve during a presentation because it is so short lived. One way to solve this problem is to produce a series of slides capturing the best possible appearance of the product as an introduction to a tasting session (see page 102). The following guidelines will help you produce a set of slides and prints for display.

1 Have a clear area set aside, near to where the food will be prepared, for the photography.

2 Prepare the background for the shot before you prepare the food product. The background should be plain so as not to detract from the food product. There should be little if any background detail visible.

Preparing the scene guarantees good results

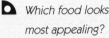

Which food looks most appealing?

3 If the product is on a plate or dish, choose a colour which provides a contrast to the main colours of the food product. Non-circular crockery – oval or octagonal – adds interest.

4 Make sure that crockery is sparkling clean and that the food product is placed on it carefully with no splashes or smears.

5 If you present the food product in a place setting, make sure all the elements are sparkling clean and do not detract from the food product.

6 Light the scene carefully so that there are no harsh highlights on the food, crockery, glasses or cutlery.

7 Some food products should be cut open to reveal the interior. Be sure to do this carefully.

8 When you have set up the background, prepare the food product. Place it within the background, check the exposure and take several shots rapidly so that you capture the 'just served' look.

9 You can capture the audience's attention by producing a series of shots which start very close in so that the nature of the product cannot be discerned, and move back in a sequence until it becomes apparent.

10 Use slide-film for presentations and print-film for a hand-round photo album.

Your presentation may have two purposes:

● to convince the client that the products are worth manufacturing;

● to help the client choose which of several possible variations should be produced.

When you have assembled a series of slides to describe the appearance of your product, you will need to write a script to accompany the slide sequence. For each slide you should make one or two key points about the product. These might be to do with the particular ingredients used, the colours achieved, the way the product will be manufactured, the sort of customer to whom the product will appeal. It is important that the sequence helps the client make decisions.

What the product tastes like

Presenting the taste of a product to the clients is an important part of convincing them that the product is worth manufacturing. You will need to provide a range of tasting experiences to help them decide which of several possible products should be manufactured. As with showing slides of the product, it is important to have a script to accompany this tasting. So for each tasting sample you should have a list of points that you want to make about the flavour and the texture.

The aim of the script and the tasting session is to help the client make decisions. It is important that the samples are laid out attractively in small portions (with tasting spoons if needed) and glasses of water to clear the palate between tastings. You should label each sample to avoid confusion, and might even add words describing key features or an attribute profile.

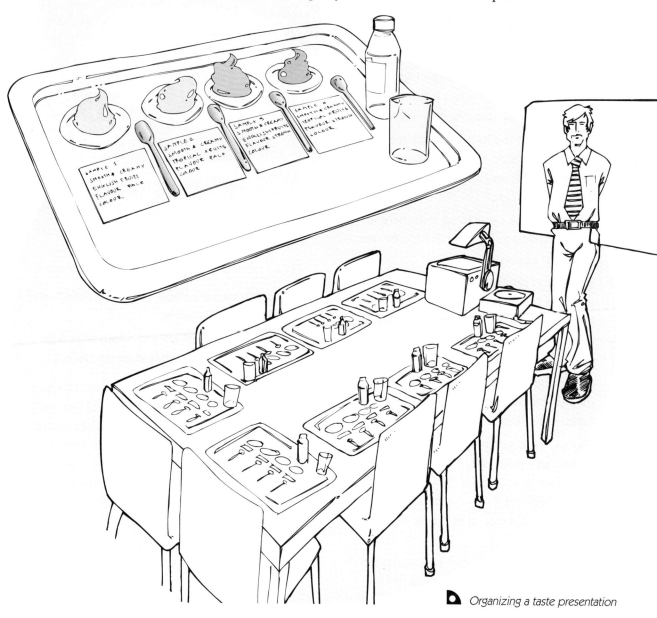

Organizing a taste presentation

What others think of the taste

It is important to demonstrate to the client that the taste and appearance of the product will appeal to the target market. This can be established through market research and you need to present the results in a way that is clear, concise and attractive. The 'raw' results will be in the form of columns of figures which are often difficult to interpret quickly and look intimidating. You should aim to turn these results into graphics which communicate well. Some examples are shown here.

The easiest way to show the client your results is by means of an overhead projector. Once you have produced a good original you can photocopy the image onto an acetate sheet. If you have used a computer to produce your graphic you can use a laser printer to print directly onto acetate sheet. If you do not have a colour printer, you can add colour to the transparencies by using overhead projector pens. You may have access to a liquid crystal display screen. You can put this on an overhead projector, just like an acetate, and project images that are being generated by a computer. This allows you to include sound and animation in your presentation.

It is worth having the information you present available as a small booklet so that the client has a copy of it for easy reference and which they can annotate during your presentation.

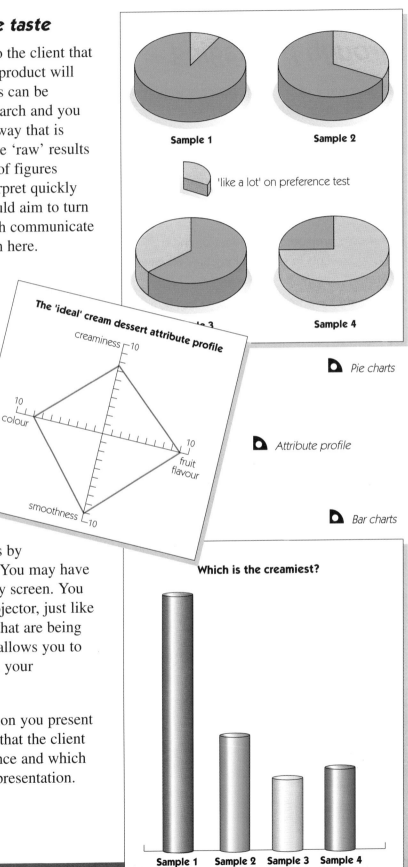

Sample 1 Sample 2

'like a lot' on preference test

Sample 4

▶ Pie charts

The 'ideal' cream dessert attribute profile

creaminess ─10

10 colour

10 fruit flavour

smoothness ─10

▶ Attribute profile

▶ Bar charts

Which is the creamiest?

Sample 1   Sample 2   Sample 3   Sample 4

Communicating through packaging

The packaging of a food product is important for four reasons.

1 It should protect the product from physical damage – nobody wants broken biscuits.

2 It should prevent the product from deteriorating – nobody wants to eat dried-out or soggy biscuits.

3 It should promote the product on the shelf – nobody wants to spend a long time finding a product to buy.

4 It should keep the product clean and fit to eat.

The packaging will play a large part in communicating the type and quality of the product to potential consumers. In deciding on the packaging for your food product you will need to take all these factors into account.

Types of packaging

There is a wide range of types of packaging available, as shown in this table.

Type of packaging	Example	
glass bottles with screw-on caps	soy sauce	1
plastic bottles with screw-on caps	soft, fizzy drinks	2
plastic squeezy bottles with flip-tops	tomato sauce	3
plastic tubs with peel-off foil lids	yoghurt	4
glass jars with screw-on lids	pickles	5
boxes with flaps	breakfast cereals	6
bags with seals	crisps	7
boxes with seals	fruit juice	8
tubes with push-in lids	Smarties	9
packets with seals	snack bars	10
cans with push-in openers	soft, fizzy drinks	11
tins with pull-off openers	sardines	12
cook-in plastic tray with film lid	ready-meals	13
foil and paper	KitKat	14
foil pouch	sports drinks	15
aerosols with valves	whipped cream	16

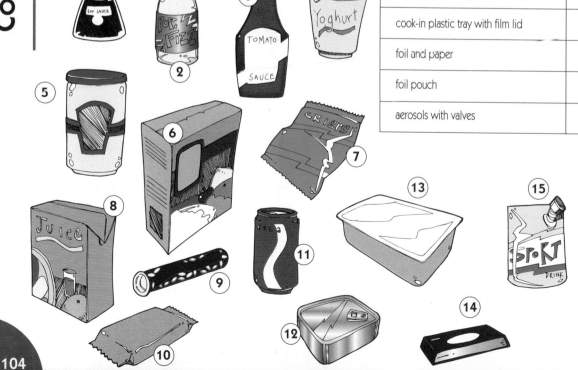

The look on the shelf

Whatever type of packaging you choose for your food product you will need to make sure that it promotes the product in an effective way. There are several features that you will need to consider.

The overall style

This is the most crucial design decision. It is linked to both the type of product and the sort of customer you see buying the product. If your product is confectionery with a broad appeal, for example, then it is important that the style is recognizable as confectionery and does not attract just a narrow section of customers. The recent advertisements for Mars bars show a range of people, from children to quite elderly people, eating the product, suggesting broad appeal. If however the product is for a particular group, as in Pepsi Max, then the style of the packaging should reflect this.

The name and brand of the product

Many food products have both a brand name and a product name – Uncle Ben's quick cook rice, Kellogg's cornflakes, Wall's sausages, Cadbury's chocolate. Some of the food products sold at supermarkets and large stores are own-brand products – Sainsbury's tomato ketchup, Tesco's beefburgers, Marks and Spencer's Indian meal for one, Boot's low-calorie dishes.

To help establish a brand identity (these cornflakes are Kellogg's cornflakes) and brand loyalty (I prefer Kellogg's cornflakes to other brands) the brand name for a particular company will usually look the same whatever product it appears on. So, the word 'Cadbury's' always looks the same – same font, same style, etc. – whatever the product. It is a major and costly decision for a company to change the look of its brand names and there have to be very good marketing reasons for doing this.

A picture of the product

Products in transparent packaging do not need a picture of the product because it is clearly visible. Products in opaque packaging sometimes need pictures of the product on the packaging to show what the product is like. Often these show the product in a serving setting and the words 'Serving suggestion only' emphasize that other ingredients and preparation time are also needed. Some products are so familiar and have such strong product identities that even though they cannot be seen, no picture is needed on the packaging. This is true for many confectionery products – Mars bars are a good example, although Smarties and M&Ms do show the product on their packaging.

The stand-out factor

Whatever style and design of packaging you produce you must ensure that it is easily recognizable, communicates the nature of the product effectively and stands out from similar rival products that will be on display in the same place.

Legal requirements

Packaging has to meet legal requirements, and these are discussed on page 207.

Producing mock-ups

You can show a client what the product will look like on the shelf by producing a packaging mock-up. Here are some guidelines.

- For thin-film wrappers use photocopies of high quality, colour originals.

- For small boxes and card sleeves draw out networks (with tabs) either by hand or by using CAD software. Print onto coloured card rather than try to colour card by hand.

- For large boxes, carefully disassemble those from existing products so that they fold out flat, add your packaging designs to the inside and reassemble inside out.

- For tins, bottles and jars, clean off the existing labels and add your own.

- For text, borders and simple images, use desk-top publishing and illustration software; print out and paste onto the mock-up.

- For illustrations of products use photocopies of coloured photographs; paste these onto the mock-up.

- Alternatively, scan coloured photographs into a computer and paste print-out onto the mock-up.

Similar products, similar packaging, yet all different

Evaluating your packaging

One way to gauge the effectiveness of your packaging is to compare it with rival commercial packaging. To do this simply collect a range of packaging from similar products that are produced commercially. Arrange this packaging on an image board and include your own design as well. Ask yourself these questions.

- Does it look slick and professional? If the answer is 'no' ask yourself how you can improve it.

- Does it have the same sort of look as the other packaging? If the answer is 'no' then you have to ask yourself whether your style is right for this type of product.

- Does it stand out? If the answer is 'no' then you have to ask yourself how you could make it more distinctive without losing its product identity.

Communicating with the maker

It is important that the way to produce the food product is communicated clearly and unambiguously. This requires careful instructions. The amount of detail in these instructions will depend on the scale of production.

Small-scale recipes for use at home

Recipes always contain the following information:

● list of ingredients;

● amount of each ingredient required to provide for a certain number;

● step-by-step instructions covering preparation details with likely time taken, cooking procedures with timings and serving suggestions.

Recipes often have a picture of the finished product and sometimes the starting ingredients. Sometimes the step-by-step instructions are illustrated.

Method

1 Sieve flour, baking powder together. Stir in sugar.

2 Beat together eggs, milk, and melted margarine and pour into the dry ingredients.

3 Mix together grated apples, cinnamon, nutmeg and lemon rind.

4 Stir into muffin mix.

5 Place in a well greased muffin tin.

6 Bake in a hot oven 220°C or gas mark 8 for 20–25 minutes until golden brown.

Large-scale recipes for use in manufacturing – Batch production

The small scale recipe for apple muffins on page 107 needs to be adapted because it takes for granted certain stages. You get to point 2 and have not melted the margarine or point 6 and have not put on the oven!

Here is a production schedule where everything is mentioned in the proper order. It ensures an efficient process.

APPLE SPICE MUFFINS PRODUCTION SCHEDULE

INGREDIENTS

200 g plain flour
2 teaspoons baking powder
75 g sugar
1 egg
250 ml milk
50 g margarine
175 g grated cooking apples
pinch of cinnamon
½ teaspoon grated lemon rind

EQUIPMENT

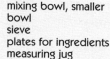

scales	teaspoon, fork,
mixing bowl, smaller	wooden spoon
bowl	peeler, sharp knife,
sieve	chopping board
plates for ingredients	grater
measuring jug	muffin tin

METHOD

Preparation

    Grease muffin tin
    Light oven 220°C, gas mark 8
    Collect equipment
    Weigh ingredients

Making

1 Sieve flour, baking powder into a mixing bowl. Stir in sugar.

2 Peel and core apples. Grate. Grate lemon. Mix together with spices.

3 Melt margarine.

4 Place milk and egg in a bowl, beat in the melted margarine. Pour into dry ingredients.

5 Stir in grated apple mixture.

6 Place equal amounts in the muffin mix.

7 Place in oven.

8 Bake for 20–25 minutes.

QUALITY ASSURANCE

Accuracy required

Grate lemon zest only, not white pith.
Stir well to distribute spice.

Do not overheat, just enough heat to melt it.

Beat well to prevent lumps. Mixture should be smooth.

Ensure well mixed.

Ensure that all are the same size.

Just above centre of oven.

Check after 20 minutes, should be well risen & golden brown.

Continuous production

For the production of very large quantities the food industry uses a continuous production line. The preparation of the materials, assembly and cooking of the product is carried out by automated machines controlled by microprocessors. The production schedule will provide instructions for the programming of the microprocessor to suit the product being manufactured. The flow chart below shows the process for the production of filled quiches.

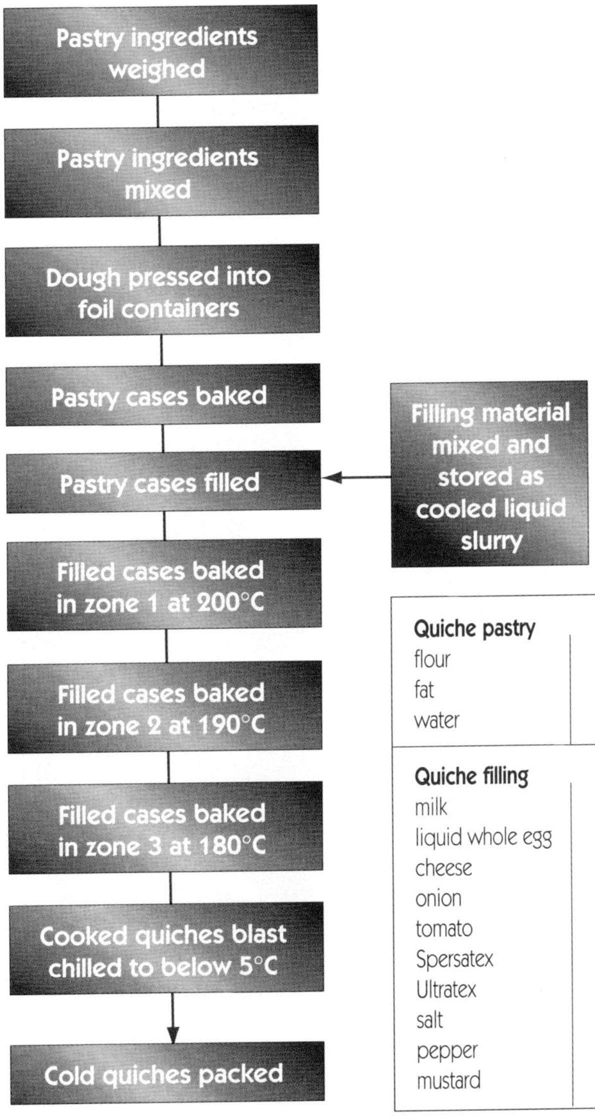

Information for both the pastry and filling ingredients is usually provided as percentages as shown in the tables. These can easily be converted into the actual amount required. Note the following features about the process:

- tolerances for weighed amounts to within +/− 3g,
- HACCP (see page 195) is built into the production schedule for storing, baking temperatures and chilling temperatures,
- the oven for cooking the filled quiche has three temperature zones; starting at a high temperature 200°C and falling to 190°C in the second zone and then to 180°C in the third zone;
- the speed of the conveyor belt will be controlled so that the time spent in each of the three zones is as required for cooking;
- the product is moved rapidly from the oven to a blast chiller which then ensures rapid cooling to a temperature at which microorganisms do not thrive.

Pastry ingredients weighed

↓

Pastry ingredients mixed

↓

Dough pressed into foil containers

↓

Pastry cases baked

↓

Pastry cases filled ← Filling material mixed and stored as cooled liquid slurry

↓

Filled cases baked in zone 1 at 200°C

↓

Filled cases baked in zone 2 at 190°C

↓

Filled cases baked in zone 3 at 180°C

↓

Cooked quiches blast chilled to below 5°C

↓

Cold quiches packed

Quiche pastry	
flour	60%
fat	30%
water	10%

Quiche filling	
milk	30%
liquid whole egg	18%
cheese	18%
onion	10%
tomato	10%
Spersatex	5.5%
Ultratex	5.5%
salt	1%
pepper	1%
mustard	1%

Communicating how to use the product

In addition to telling the consumer about the type of product and providing nutritional and storage information (see page 207), the packaging may need to provide instructions on how to prepare the food product for eating. It is important that these instructions are clear and unambiguous. Other information you might find includes:

- conventional cooking and microwave cooking instructions;

- whether or not the product is suitable for home-freezing;

- instructions on defrosting or cooking from frozen;

- a recipe in which the product can be used.

Some products are supported by the sale of recipe books which show how to produce particular dishes using the product. All this information helps to make the product more attractive to the consumer.

Examples of all these types of user support are shown in the panel below. You may develop some examples of these as part of your designing and making with food.

User support for food products

Food products for special diets

Diabetics

Who is it for?

- Those who suffer from diabetes.

What are the important background facts?

- A common complaint affecting around 2 per cent of the population.
- Develops at any age and continues throughout life.
- Diabetes stops the body from producing enough/any insulin – a hormone that helps the body use sugar in the blood for energy.
- Diabetics must keep blood sugar level normal and keep their weight down.
- A drop in blood sugar level can cause hypoglycaemia. The diabetic may go into a coma. Treatment is to give an easily absorbed form of sugar.

What is their situation?

- Generally, most diabetics are able to control their condition through careful eating patterns, which encompass many of the healthy eating guidelines.
- Usually, diabetics have to monitor their blood sugar level regularly (by testing blood or urine) and give themselves injections of insulin.
- Provided that diabetics follow the guidance of their clinical dietician, the condition is controllable and not debilitating.

What is already on the market?

What are the nutritional needs?

- A well-balanced diet taking foods from all food groups.
- Avoid high sugar content foods.
- Use sources of soluble fibre to help regulate blood sugar level.
- Carbohydrate intake must be controlled.

Resources checklist
Knowledge and understanding of the problem: • nutritional requirements of diabetics;   • need for regular meals and sugar intake;   • diabetic food market.
Knowledge and understanding for the solution: • use of artificial sweeteners;   • use of exchange system to keep blood sugar level normal.
Useful strategies: • image boards;   • attribute analysis;   • interviews;   • evaluation by user trip;   • evaluation by attribute profile;   • evaluation by appropriateness.

Design guides – for special diets

Vegetarians

Who is it for?

- People who do not eat meat.

What are the important background facts?

- There are different types of vegetarian – lacto-ovo, lacto, vegan, fruitarians.
- There are different reasons why people become vegetarians – moral, religious, economic, environmental, ecological.
- The number of people choosing to eat less meat or become vegetarian has increased in recent years; 7 per cent of the UK population now claim to be vegetarian.
- There is a growing market for vegetarian food products.
- Increasing numbers of young people choose vegetarian diets.

What is their situation?

- Difficult to generalize as vegetarians come from all races, classes and backgrounds.
- Usually interested in a healthy life style and concerned about environmental and ecological issues.
- If they do not understand basic nutrition they may stop eating some foods without replacing the nutrients they provide.

What is already on the market?

What are the nutritional needs?

- Vegetarians have the same nutritional needs as everyone else.
- It is important to ensure that the combination of foods eaten provides for a balanced diet and meets nutritional requirements.
- Vitamin and mineral supplements may be necessary (e.g. B12, A and D, and calcium for vegans).
- Absorption of iron may be poor in vegetarians, leading to anaemia.

Resources checklist

Knowledge and understanding of the problem:
- nutritional requirements for differing types of vegetarians;
- the types of foods that the various sorts of vegetarians do and do not eat.

Knowledge and understanding for the solution:
- nutritional qualities and limitations of fruit and vegetables;
- cooking methods suitable for vegetarian food;
- finishing methods to enhance appearance of vegetarian food;
- storage/contamination risks;
- packaging suitable for vegetarian products.

Useful strategies:
- image boards;
- attribute analysis;
- interviews;
- evaluation by user trip;
- evaluation by attribute profile;
- evaluation by appropriateness.

Weight watchers

Who is it for?

- People who are trying to lose weight.

What are the important background facts?

- One-third of all women in the UK and half of all men are overweight.
- The number of people that are overweight is more now than it was five years ago.
- Overweight is defined as having a body mass index (BMI) over 25.
  BMI = weight (kg)/height squared (m^2).
- Health risks increase as BMI increases.
- Risks include high blood pressure, high blood cholesterol, diabetes, coronary heart disease, respiratory disease, gallstones and some cancers.
- Weight can be reduced by increased energy expenditure as well as reduced energy intake, so exercise improves success.

What is their situation?

- There is considerable pressure to be slim, which can lead overweight people to feel unhappy about their personal appearance.
- Some people diet to excess and become very ill both physically and mentally.
- In dieting, body fat should be reduced, not lean tissue.
- A maximum of 2 kg weight loss per week is acceptable.
- All foods can be eaten in moderation.
- Crash diets are not the answer.
- Eating a wide range of foods in moderation coupled with exercise is the best way to lose weight.

What is already on the market?

What are the nutritional needs?

- The amount of energy needed depends on the individual, amount overweight and usual energy expenditure.
- Total calories taken in per day should be between 1000 and 1500.
- Diet should contain adequate amounts of essential nutrients, but be lower in energy value.
- Foods should be of high nutritional density and low energy density.
- Foods from all main groups should be eaten.
- High carbohydrate / low-fat diets are recommended.

Resources checklist

Knowledge and understanding of the problem:
- the market for diet foods;
- the health risks associated with being overweight;
- the health risks associated with over dieting.

Knowledge and understanding for the solution:
- basic nutritional requirements;
- packaging suitable for diet products;
- storage/contamination risks.

Useful strategies:
- PIES;
- image boards;
- attribute analysis;
- interviews;
- evaluation by preference tests;
- evaluation by attribute profile;
- evaluation by appropriateness.

Food products for the very young

Weaning food

Who is it for?

- Babies from 0 to 12 months – covering introductory foods (rusks, puréed fruit, etc.) through to weaning babies onto proper solid foods.

What is their situation?

- Parents may be concerned about the additives and preservatives in some commercially produced weaning foods.
- Many parents want to use fresh foods and prepare their own weaning foods at home.

What is already on the market?

What are the important background facts?

- Young children are dependent on their parent(s) for everything, including the food they eat.
- A balanced, healthy diet, even when very young, is crucial to ensure healthy growth of limbs and organs and development of mental and physical abilities.
- There are concerns that high sugar and salt intake in young children can be damaging.
- Children's attitudes to food – likes and dislikes – can be moulded when very young. They need a broad, well-balanced variety of foods.

What are the nutritional needs?

RNI chart as bar graphs for the following nutrients for each age group in months

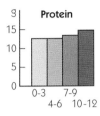

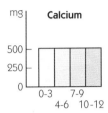

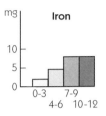

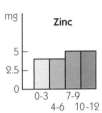

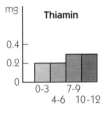

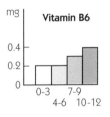

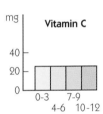

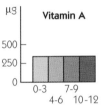

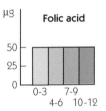

- Continuing importance of milk for calcium, protein and dietary energy – should still be either breast milk or infant milk powder (formula milk).
- High-fibre, low-fat diets recommended for adults are not suitable for children, so fibre-rich foods should be introduced with care.
- Foods need to be calorie and nutrient dense.
- Balanced vitamin intake is crucial.

Resources checklist

Knowledge and understanding of the problem:
- the 'breast v. bottle' debate;
- cooking methods available to parents in the home;
- particular requirements of babies – low sugar, low salt;
- the infant food market.

Knowledge and understanding for the solution:
- portion requirement;
- nutrient-dense foods;
- storage/contamination risks;
- costing and pricing;
- packaging;
- labelling and instructional information.

Useful strategies:
- PIES;
- using books and magazines;
- questionnaire;
- evaluation by user trip.

Food products for the elderly

Meals-on-wheels

Who is it for?

What are the important background facts?

- Decline in community care facilities and increased reliance on voluntary organizations.
- Decline of 'corner shop' and extended family in some communities.
- Decline in availability of public transport in many areas.
- Mobility/dexterity problems associated with age-related medical complaints (arthritis, rheumatism, etc.).
- Possibility of emotional stress due to bereavement, ill health, loneliness.

- Possibility of limited income.
- Large-scale catering for the elderly – central production and distribution centres.

What is their situation?

- Living conditions: possibly widowed, living alone perhaps in accommodation that is difficult to manage.
- Concern at loss of independence.
- Concern at loss of physical abilities.
- Limited cooking and storage facilities.
- Mobility difficulties leading to problems with shopping.

What is already on the market?

Resources checklist

Knowledge and understanding of the problem:
- local meals-on-wheels provision;
- the part of the main meal in the diet;
- the significance of the delivery.

Knowledge and understanding for the solution:
- production systems;
- portion requirement;
- nutrient-dense foods;
- storage/contamination risks;
- costing and pricing.

Useful strategies:
- image boards;
- interviews;
- evaluation by user trip;
- evaluation by preference tests.

What are the nutritional needs?

- Elderly people are generally less physically active so their appetites are smaller and they eat less.
- Energy requirements may reduce, but vitamin/mineral requirement remains the same or may even increase.

EAR bar chart for older age groups

M - males   F - females

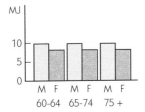
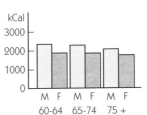

RNI bar chart for age group 50+ years
M - males   F - females

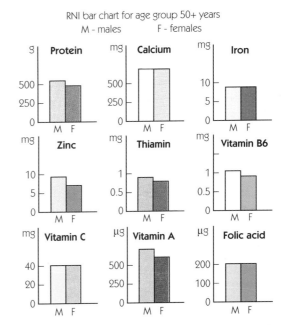

Food products for those at risk

Students

Who is it for?

Resources checklist

Knowledge and understanding of the problem:
- money available;
- the part that different meals play in the diet;
- the significance of eating when you are alone;
- equipment and skills available.

Knowledge and understanding for the solution:
- nutrient-dense foods;
- low-cost sources of protein;
- packaging, labelling and instructions;
- storage/contamination risks;
- costing and pricing.

Useful strategies:
- image boards;
- attribute analysis;
- interviews;
- evaluation by user trip;
- evaluation by preference tests;
- evaluation by attribute profile.

What are the important background facts?

- Decrease in student grants, bursaries, student loans.
- Likely to be living away from family, so lack of family support.
- Student life is often multicultural.
- Not always possible to supplement income.

What is their situation?

- Income is likely to be low.
- Possibly variable eating patterns; meals eaten irregularly and late at night.
- Variable accommodation.
- Limited cooking resources.
- Possibly a high-energy life style – sport, dancing, travel.

What is already on the market?

What are the nutritional needs?

- Should cut down on fats and sugar to avoid overweight.
- Should maintain or increase protein, vitamins and minerals to promote health.

EAR bar chart for people aged 19-50

M - males   F - females

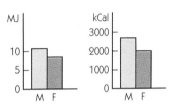

RNI bar chart for age group 19-50 years
M - males   F - females

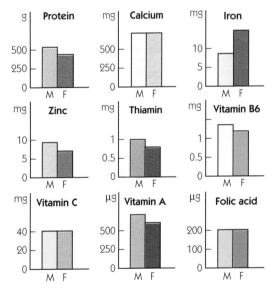

Earthquake victims

Who is it for?

What are the important background facts?

- Areas of the world at risk from earthquakes.
- The effects of earthquakes on transport, services, buildings, people, housing, land and population.
- 'After' quakes.

What is their situation?

- In a state of shock.
- Possibly injured, maybe seriously.
- Living in the open, possibility of exposure.
- Little or no food.
- Contaminated water supplies.
- Poor communications and transport.
  - Few facilities for cooking.
    - Danger from 'after' quakes.

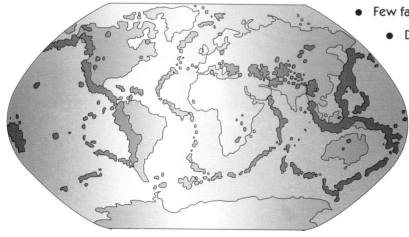

What is already on the market?

- Dehydrated energy-dense foods and drinks as used by the armed services and outdoor pursuits enthusiasts.

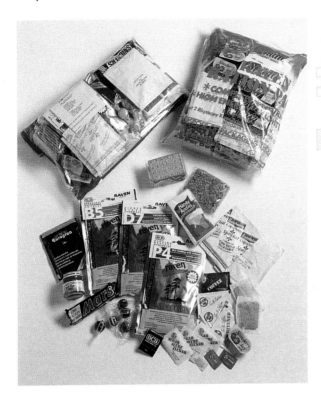

What are the nutritional needs?

- Clean water supply.
- High calorie intake.
- Hot food and drink provide comfort and prevent food poisoning.
- High protein intake to promote recovery from injury.
- High vitamin and mineral intake to promote good health.
- Food and drink should be energy dense, easy to eat and easy to digest.
- Drinks and fresh, clean water.
- Balanced diet, good range of foods.

Resources checklist

Knowledge and understanding of the problem:
- the effects of hypothermia;
- local conditions, particularly the availability of materials for building shelter and dry wood for fuel.

Knowledge and understanding for the solution:
- writing easy-to-follow instructions;
- nutrient-dense foods;
- dehydration and other preservation techniques;
- packaging techniques and instructions;
- storage/contamination risks.

Useful strategies:
- attribute analysis
- evaluation by user trip
- evaluation by attribute profile
- evaluation by appropriateness

Food products from primary foods

Eggs

Where will they be sold and who are they for?

Resources checklist

Knowledge and understanding of the problem:
- dietary requirements of vegetarians;
- cultural preferences of some vegetarian groups;
- nutritional qualities of eggs.

Knowledge and understanding for the solution:
- hygienic and safe preparation of egg-based products;
- storage/contamination risks;
- packaging suitable for cook-chill products.

Useful strategies:
- image boards;
- brainstorming;
- interviews;
- evaluation by preference tests;
- evaluation by attribute profile.

What are the important background facts?

- There is an increase in vegetarian consumers who want suitable food products.
- At present there is a lack of variety of egg-based products.
- Eggs are an inexpensive, rich source of protein, iron, vitamin D and other nutrients; particularly suitable for young children.
- There have been health scares relating to food poisoning from salmonella in eggs.
- The sale of eggs is declining.

What types of products does the supermarket sell already?

- quiche-based flans;
- vegetable and cheese pies;
- cheeseburgers;
- cheese and onion patties.

What types of products might they develop?

- egg-based curries;
- pancakes filled with fruit/vegetables;
- sauce-based products using eggs and fresh vegetables;
- eggs and fresh fish bake;
- roulades made from vegetables;
- egg and winter salad, stuffed egg salad;
- egg and mushroom savoury;
- flavoured custard, meringue, mousse and cream desserts.

What are the nutritional issues?

- The structure and nutritional composition of eggs.
- The nutritive importance of eggs in the diet.
- The protein requirements of children and adults.

Quorn®

Where will it be sold and who is it for?

Resources checklist

Knowledge and understanding of the problem:
- dietary requirements of vegetarians;
- cultural preferences of some vegetarian groups;
- nutritional qualities of Quorn®;
- flavour and texture limitations of Quorn®.

Knowledge and understanding for the solution:
- storage/contamination risks;
- cafeteria procedures for serving hot dishes;
- means of enhancing bland flavours and dull textures.

Useful strategies:
- image boards;
- brainstorming;
- attribute analysis;
- interviews;
- evaluation by preference tests;
- evaluation by attribute profile.

What are the important background facts?

- Quorn® is suitable for vegetarians.
- Quorn® is made from myco-protein and consists of protein, carbohydrates, fats, fibre and sodium.
- There are several different types of Quorn® available.
- Quorn® is similar in price to chicken.

What types of products does the cafeteria sell already?

- cheese and egg salad;
- cheese and onion quiche and pasties;
- vegetable curry;
- vegetable casserole;
- vegetable lasagne.

What types of products might they develop?

- minced Quorn®, mushroom and sauce pie;
- diced Quorn®, vegetable and herb hotpot;
- paté with creamed Quorn®, shrimps and tartar sauce;
- pasta bake with Quorn®, red peppers, mushrooms and peas;
- crispy fried patties with minced Quorn®, cheese, potatoes and chives;
- lasagne with minced Quorn® and vegetables;
- Quorn®, leek and rice au gratin.

What are the nutritional issues?

- The nutritional qualities and limitations of Quorn® in the diet.
- Proteins not eaten by vegetarians.
- The types of proteins in different foods.

Potatoes

Where will they be sold and who are they for?

What are the important background facts?

- Range of products that can be made in the centre. This will depend on the facilities for preparation and storage.
- Value-for-money compared with other foods.
- Popularity of potato-based dishes.

What types of products does the leisure centre sell already?

- sandwiches and rolls;
- soft drinks, hot drinks;
- crisps, peanuts;
- meat and cheese pasties.

Resources checklist

Knowledge and understanding of the problem:
- preferences of leisure centre users;
- nutritional qualities of potatoes;
- flavour and texture limitations of potatoes.

Knowledge and understanding for the solution:
- storage/contamination risks;
- leisure centre procedures for serving hot dishes;
- means of enhancing bland flavours and dull textures.

Useful strategies:
- image boards;
- brainstorming;
- interviews;
- questionnaires;
- evaluation by preference tests;
- evaluation by attribute profile.

What types of products might they develop?

- range of baked potato fillings;
- sauté potatoes;
- cheese and sweetcorn potato cakes;
- hot dog potatoes;
- leek and potato soup with fresh rolls;
- scalloped potatoes with nutmeg.

What are the nutritional issues?

- The nutritional qualities and limitations of different sorts of potatoes.
- Frying potatoes – the addition of fat.
- Retaining the vitamin C in preparation.

100g boiled Potatoes = 80 Kcal or 33KJ

100g chipped Potatoes = 234 Kcal or 989KJ

ITS UP TO YOU.

Food products from the bakery

For sale at the bakery

Where will it be sold and who is it for?

What are the important background facts?

- Wheat growing is major industry in some countries.
- Nearly everyone in the UK eats bread.
- There is concern about the effect on health of 'modern' highly refined white bread.
- There are many different breads from other cultures.
- There are areas of the world where bread is a traditional staple food.

What types of products do they sell already?

- large loaves, rolls – large, soft, small, crusty, bridge;
- small/large buns (plain, iced, Chelsea, Swedish tea ring);
- pizzas – cheese, tomato.

What types of products might they develop?

- large savoury buns (black/green olive, onion, tomato, etc.);
- small sweet buns (cinnamon/spice, cherries, dried apricots);
- bread products enriched with eggs and sugar;
- bread products with additional ingredients – olives, dates, chopped peppers.

What are the nutritional issues?

- The role of cereals as a staple food.
- The nutritional content of cereals.
- Types of flour: wholemeal, wheatmeal, brown, white, granary.
- The role of fibre in the diet.

Design guides – from the bakery

For sale in a tea shop

Where will it be sold and who is it for?

What are the important background facts?

- National Trust tea shops are sited in stately homes and gardens; opening hours vary.
- There is a wide range of customers – children, adults and the elderly – requiring drinks, drinks and snacks, full meals.
- The shops have different catering facilities.

What types of products do they sell already?

- sponge cakes (jam, chocolate) to serve with afternoon tea and morning coffee;
- biscuits;
- jam tarts and sausage rolls;
- scones.

What types of products might they develop?

- Products that can be frozen/stored in bulk to retain quality/freshness.
- Fresh yeast-based products, e.g. hot cross buns, apple strudel, kuchen, Chelsea buns.
- Different prices and greater range of portion sizes, individual products and ones to be sliced into portions.
- Basic cakes that can be decorated to demand, e.g. whisked sponge, Victoria sandwich, Madeira cake, ginger cake.
- Cakes and pastries from other cultures.

What are the nutritional issues?

- The place of flour-based products in the diet.
- The effects of too high a proportion of flour products in the diet.
- The effect of high fat/sugar intake on obesity/dental caries.
- High-fibre flours.
- Modifications that can help reduce fat and sugar content and add fibre.

Resources checklist

Knowledge and understanding of the problem:
- local preferences for breads, cakes and pastries;
- nutritional qualities of baked products.

Knowledge and understanding for the solution:
- bread, pastry and cake recipes from around the world;
- small-scale catering techniques;
- storage and staling;
- finishing techniques.

Useful strategies:
- attribute analysis;
- interviews;
- questionnaires;
- evaluation by preference tests;
- evaluation by attribute profile.

For breakfast in a coffee shop

Where will it be sold and who is it for?

Resources checklist

Knowledge and understanding of the problem:
- preferences of coffee shop users;
- nutritional issues associated with fried foods.

Knowledge and understanding for the solution:
- storage/contamination risks;
- cafeteria procedures for serving hot dishes.

Useful strategies:
- PIES;
- attribute analysis;
- interviews;
- questionnaires;
- evaluation by user trips;
- evaluation by attribute profile.

What are the important background facts?

- The requirements of the customers.
- Opening times of coffee shop, advertising, position and layout.
- Price range of food products, special price deal.

What types of products does the coffee shop sell already?

- fried breakfast (eggs/bacon/tomatoes);
- scrambled/poached eggs on toast;
- cereals, toast and preserves;
- coffee and tea.

What types of products might they develop?

- range of savoury/sweet-filled pancakes;
- muffins, waffles, scotch pancakes, potato cakes;
- hot brioches with butter;
- filled omelettes, kedgeree;
- range of fruit/vegetable juices;
- special muesli and fresh fruit.

What are the nutritional issues?

- What nutrients are best eaten at the beginning of the day?
- The importance of breakfast as a main meal of the day.
- The metabolic rate of the body.
- Problems related to high-fat diets and fried foods.

Design guides – from a confectioner

Food products from a confectioner

Sweetmeats and desserts

Where will they be sold and who are they for?

Resources checklist

Knowledge and understanding of the problem:
- nutritional qualities of sugar-based desserts;
- local preferences for desserts;
- flavours/textures likely to compliment highly spiced main course dishes.

Knowledge and understanding for the solution:
- sugar-based dessert recipes from around the world;
- qualities of different types of sugar;
- cooking procedures appropriate for using sugar;
- finishing techniques;
- sugar alternatives.

Useful strategies:
- using books and magazines;
- attribute analysis;
- evaluation by ranking;
- evaluation by difference testing;
- evaluation by attribute profile.

What are the important background facts?

- Food customs from other cultures.
- The increased leisure opportunities in society.
- The requirements of the customers.

What types of products does the restaurant sell already?

- potato halva – sweetmeat made from sugar, milk and potato;
- flooda – sweet served as a drink;
- vattalappam – rich, spicy coconut custard;
- ras fulas – sweetmeat made from balls of cream cheese simmered in sugar syrup.

What types of products might they develop?

Sweetmeats, desserts and biscuits based on:

- cereals/nuts, e.g. phlimi (creamy rice pudding), vermicelli pudding, kalfi (ice-cream with nuts), soojee halva (semolina/cinnamon), semolina luddo, nan khatai (a crisp semolina shortbread);
- fruits and vegetables, e.g. gujar halva (carrots), spiced baked bananas, peach and lemon mousse, fruit-filled pancakes;
- chocolate/cream/milk, e.g. chocolate fondue, banana cream, chocolate sponge fingers, goolab jamoon (sugar/milk).

What are the nutritional issues?

- The role of sugar in the diet.
- Effects on the body of a high-sugar diet.
- Modifications that can help reduce fat and sugar content.

Sweets

Where will it be sold and who is it for?

What are the important background facts?

- Sweets as a luxury food product.
- Commercial advertising and its effect on the consumer.
- Special occasion food products.

What types of products does the stall sell already?

- toffees, butterscotch drops, chocolate drops;
- sweets based on cereals and coconut;
- peppermint creams.

Resources checklist

Knowledge and understanding of the problem:
- different types of sweets that are available on the market;
- role of sweets in the diet.

Knowledge and understanding for the solution:
- sweet recipes from around the world;
- qualities of different types of sugar;
- cooking procedures appropriate for sugar;
- sugar alternatives;
- packaging for sweets.

Useful strategies:
- using books and magazines;
- brainstorming;
- attribute analysis;
- evaluation by ranking;
- evaluation by difference testing;
- evaluation by attribute profile.

What types of products might they develop?

- toffee-based products;
- nut/fruit-based products, e.g. nut fudge, almond candies, almond butter crisp, raisin and nut and rum fudge, fruit and nut bars, lemon creams;
- chocolate/coconut-based products, e.g. rum chocolate truffles, chocolate caramels, chocolate eggs, coconut bars, coconut ice;
- marzipan bites.

What are the nutritional issues?

- Problems associated with high sugar and fat content of sweets – obesity and dental caries.
- People's preferences, special occasions, comfort foods.
- Relationship between diabetics and sweets.
- Young children and development of a 'craving' for sweets.

Design guides – from a confectioner

Ice-cream

Where will it be sold and who is it for?

What are the important background facts?

- Increasing market for ice-creams in leisure industry.
- The healthy eating lobby.
- Food hygiene and safety regulations with high-risk food products.

What types of products does the ice-cream bar sell already?

- vanilla, chocolate, strawberry, raspberry ripple ice-cream;
- ice-cream in cornets and tubs.

What types of products might they develop?

- variations of basic mix – honey, caramel, mango;
- toppers for the ice-creams – crushed/chopped nuts, chocolate chips, crushed health bars, crushed biscuits;
- fresh-fruit bases – strawberry, raspberry, peach, banana, pineapple, melon;
- sherbets, sorbets and ices – orange, lemon, cherries, ice-milk;
- health-conscious products – sugar-free ice-creams, frozen yoghurts, frozen fruit juices.

What are the nutritional issues?

- High sugar/fat content of many ice-creams.
- Modifications that can be made – use sugar alternatives, low-fat milks and creams, low-fat yoghurts, carob.
- Addition of fresh fruits and nuts for vitamins and fibre.

Resources checklist

Knowledge and understanding of the problem:
- the ice-cream market;
- nutritional qualities if products based on ice-cream.

Knowledge and understanding for the solution:
- a range of ice-cream recipes;
- small-scale catering techniques;
- techniques for the production of solid, foam-based food products;
- freezing as a method of preservation;
- shelf-life and storage.

Useful strategies:
- PIES;
- using books and magazines;
- attribute analysis;
- evaluation by ranking;
- evaluation by difference testing;
- evaluation by attribute profile.

Maintaining quality

It is essential that food products do not cause harm to those who consume them. One way of ensuring that this is the case is to apply HACCP to the production process. This is described in more detail on page 195. There is of course far more to being a quality product than not being harmful. A tin of baked beans in which all the beans are broken up and become mushy might not be harmful but it would be unacceptable to most consumers. The food industry has to find ways of assuring quality.

How do they do this?

The key to **quality assurance** is the setting of a standard which the product has to meet. The required standards are usually identified by the product development team and then written into the specification. It is the food manufacturers' responsibility to ensure that the standards are maintained. How does the manufacturer do this? It is here that **quality control** is important. The food manufacturer can set up the manufacturing process so that the requirements of the standard are met and then monitor the product during, and at the end of manufacture to ensure that these standards have in fact been maintained.

There are many different ways to carry out this quality control. Some involve the careful measuring of amounts of ingredients and this can be checked by regular random sampling to ensure that the required amounts of ingredients are being used to within agreed tolerances. Some involve the careful use of additives to ensure that the food behaves in a particular way. You may have heard that vegetables take longer to cook in hard water areas than in soft water areas. This is because hard water contains calcium ions and these have the effect of stiffening the cell walls so that vegetable stay crunchier. Addition of calcium ions is used to maintain the crispness of food products describes as containing 'crunchy' vegetables. Of course just the right amount has to be added. Too little and there will be no added crunchiness; too much would be uneconomical and might be detrimental to the taste! Knowing how much to add and ensuring that this amount is added is quality control in action.

What does this mean to me?

When you are developing a food product you have responsibility to set the standard. You can do this by developing a detailed specification. That is your quality assurance statement. When you write the production schedule you can build in elements of quality control. Often these will be in the form of instructions which require judgment on the part of the maker, e.g., heat and stir until the sauce thickens. Unless you indicate how thick the sauce has to become then this statement will not help quality control. A better description would be; heat and stir until the sauce is the consistency of pouring cream. Now the maker has the information required to practise quality control.

7 Food chemistry

Why is food chemistry important?

When you design and make food products you can use existing recipes, adapt recipes or make up your own recipes. The success of the new product will depend not only on your cooking skills but also on using your knowledge of food to choose the right ingredients. When you adapt a recipe or devise a new one you need to ask yourself 'What might happen if?'. For example:

- What might happen if I change the amount of flour in a sauce?
- What might happen if I add more sugar to a biscuit mix?
- What might happen if I fry rather than boil the vegetables?
- What might happen if I add egg to the filling?

A knowledge of how food behaves when it is cut, mixed or heated will help you answer these questions and make sensible design decisions. If things don't go quite as expected, it can also help you to explain why.

What's in food?

Most of the foods we eat are complex mixtures of chemical compounds, though these compounds fall into only three different groups:

- carbohydrates;
- fats;
- protein.

Two other sorts of compound are important for health: vitamins and minerals.

Composition of carbohydrates

Carbohydrates are made from the elements carbon, hydrogen and oxygen. 'Carbohydrates' means 'compound of carbon and water', and their chemical formula can be written as $C(H_2O)n$. They are formed in the green leaves of plants by the process of photosynthesis in which carbon dioxide reacts with water to produce carbohydrates and oxygen gas. Some carbohydrates taste sweet and are soluble in water. These are sugars. Glucose, sucrose (the sugar used in cooking) and lactose (found in milk) are the most common sugars.

Plants use some of the glucose produced in photosynthesis to make starch. Hundreds of glucose molecules are joined to form one starch molecule. This process is called **condensation polymerization** because the joining of two glucose molecules is always accompanied by the loss of a water molecule.

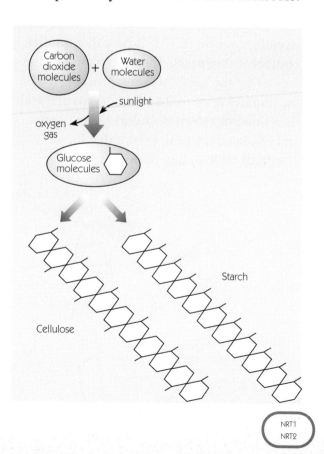

🔵 *Plants make giant molecules from small molecules*

NRT1
NRT2

The starch that is formed is called a **polysaccharide** which means 'many sugars'. Starch is insoluble in water so it can act as a store of glucose which can be released when the plant needs it. Starch from plants is used in many foods and is a source of energy for humans as well.

Plants also join up glucose molecules in other ways, one of which produces **cellulose**. Cellulose has a different structure from starch and is used by plants to make the walls of cells and to give them strength and rigidity. Cellulose cannot be digested by the human body. It is called **dietary fibre** or **NSP** (non-starch polysaccharide).

If you look at potato cells under the microscope you can see the cell walls made from cellulose and the starch granules inside the cell.

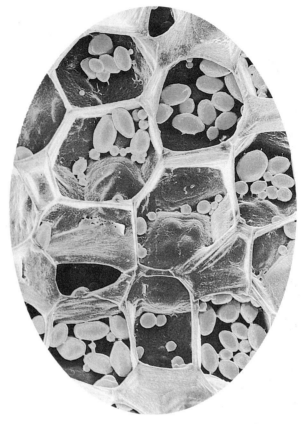

Starch and cellulose in potato cells

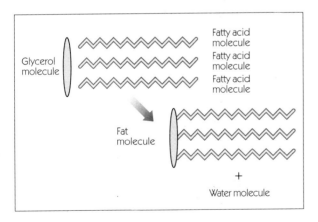

Fats are made from glycerol and fatty acids

Composition of fats

Fats are also made up of the elements carbon, hydrogen and oxygen but the atoms are arranged in a completely different way. Fat molecules have two components – **glycerol** and **fatty acids**. Some fatty acids are called **saturated fatty acids** because the carbon atoms are saturated with hydrogen atoms. These are found in fats from animal sources, such as butter and lard, and are solid and hard at room temperature. Some fatty acids are called **polyunsaturated fatty acids** because they are not completely saturated with hydrogen atoms. These are found in fats from plant sources such as sunflowers, peanuts and corn. They are soft or liquid fats at room temperature.

Composition of protein

Protein contains the elements carbon, hydrogen, oxygen and nitrogen and sometimes the elements sulphur, phosphorus and iron. All protein molecules are made up of small **amino acid** molecules joined together in a long chain. Protein molecules may contain any number from 50 to several thousand amino acid units. There are thousands of different proteins and each one is unique, but there are only 20 amino acids commonly found in foods. Eight amino acids *must* be eaten by adults because they cannot be made by the body. These are called **indispensible amino acids**. They are:

- valine
- leucine
- isoleucine
- threonine
- lysine
- phenylalanine
- tryptophan
- methionine

Children need a ninth indespensible acid called histidine.

The other amino acids are called **dispensible amino acids** because they can be made by the body. They include:

- glycine
- aspartic acid
- alanine
- cysteine

The amount of each amino acid and the order in which they are arranged in the protein molecule is different for each sort of protein. This is why the protein in eggs is different from the protein in meat. The important proteins in foods are:

- casein in cheese;
- caseinagen in milk;
- glutelin and gliadin in wheat;
- ovalbumin in egg;
- collagen and elastin in meat.

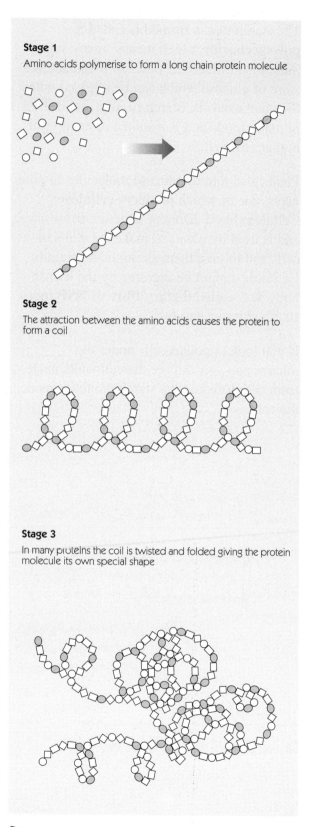

Stage 1
Amino acids polymerise to form a long chain protein molecule

Stage 2
The attraction between the amino acids causes the protein to form a coil

Stage 3
In many proteins the coil is twisted and folded giving the protein molecule its own special shape

Formation of a protein molecule from amino acids

Food chemistry in action

How can I get food to go brown?

Sugar is affected by heat. On heating with water it dissolves to give a syrup. On further heating the water boils off and the syrup becomes thicker and gets darker, changing from light to dark brown. In this chemical reaction, called **caramelization**, the carbohydrate molecules react together to form more complex substances. The syrup tastes less sweet and develops a slightly 'burnt' taste. You can use caramelized sugar to add colour and flavour to custard desserts and to make toffee.

A brown colour is also obtained when carbohydrate and protein are both present. Dry heat from grilling, baking or frying will cause a complex chemical reaction to take place so that a brown colour is produced. This happens when bread, cakes, nuts and roasted meats are cooked. A high temperature is needed and therefore it is only the outside of the food that becomes brown – the inside rarely gets hot enough. So chips, cakes and roast meat are brown on the outside only. This is called the Maillard reaction, after the Frenchman who discovered it.

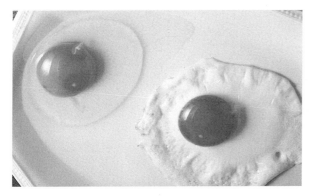

Protein coagulation through heat

Two ways to get browning – the Maillard reaction and caramelization

How can I make my mixture set?

You can make semi-solid or liquid foods set by using protein, or by using starch.

Protein sets

Protein will set a liquid by coagulation. This happens when proteins, such as ovalbumen in eggs, are heated. At room temperature the long-chain protein molecules are arranged in coils folded up in complex arrangements. On heating, these long molecules begin to unfold, bump into one another and form new bonds between each other.

You can see coagulation taking place easily when an egg is heated. The liquid, colourless egg white changes to a solid white between 60°C and 70°C. This is because the protein molecules are more densely clustered together and deflect light so that the egg white is no longer translucent, it is opaque. On further heating the liquid yellow yolk changes to a yellow solid.

Effect of overheating on protein set

The process of coagulation is used to set the filling of quiches and to make an egg custard. As the mixture is heated the protein molecules form a loose network which can hold water in many small pockets. But the protein set can be ruined by overheating. Excess heat will cause the loose network of protein molecules to contract and squeeze out the water that was being held.

You can see this when you overcook scrambled egg. The egg and milk mixture begins to set as you stir the mixture over a medium heat. The mixture sets and is dry and fluffy and ready to eat. But extra heat will cause a thin liquid to be squeezed out of the mixture and it becomes tough and rubbery. This often occurs when cooking scrambled eggs, and sometimes happens in egg custards that are over-cooked.

Gelatine, another protein, can be used to make liquids set (see page 86). It is an animal product and is not used by vegetarians. In the production of yoghurt it is the action of acid that causes protein molecules to coagulate.

Starch sets

Starch thickens a liquid by a process called **gelatinization**. For this to take place, heat and water are needed. When a starch grain is put in cold water it does not dissolve, it just sinks to the bottom. On heating, the water molecules force their way into the grain, releasing long starch molecules into the water. These molecules cause the water to become more viscous and this thicker consistency is the texture required for a pouring sauce. As the liquid cools the long molecules form a loose network throughout the liquid which traps water in small pockets. When cool, the liquid sets into a gel.

How can I make a mixture light and fluffy in texture?

You can make mixtures light and fluffy by incorporating air into the mixture. This is sometimes called making a **foam**.

You can use the proteins in egg white to produce excellent foams. Their volume can be increased by as much as eight times by beating in air. When an egg white is beaten, the large protein molecules unfold and bond to each other at the interface between the liquid egg white and the air. In this way air bubbles are formed, enclosed by a wall of protein. The protein molecules form a delicate network preventing the tiny air bubbles from joining up into large bubbles.

Adding a foam like this to a food product gives it a light, fluffy texture, but the foam can be affected by fat. Fat interferes with the formation of a foam and a single drop of egg yolk which contains fat can reduce the egg white foam's maximum volume by as much as two-thirds. So it is important not to get any egg yolk in the egg white when you are separating the white from the yolk.

▶ Egg white foams have a large volume and give products a light texture

Once you have made a foam you can use it to give a light texture to food products. You can fold it into egg yolks to make a mousse or into a mixture containing fat to make a soufflé. The foam in contact with the fat will slowly break down, but the mixture has already been filled with air bubbles. Folding in carefully is important, as mechanical action such as stirring can break down the foam by causing the bubbles of air to merge (coalesce).

If you heat the foam then the protein molecules will coagulate or set forming a solid network. The liquid foam is now a solid foam, as in a meringue or a soufflé.

Getting liquids to stay mixed

You can find out about emulsions on page 86.

Food chemistry

Food tests

It is important to be able to identify the types of compounds in food. This is done using chemical tests. In food-testing laboratories, scientists can not only test for which types of compounds are present – carbohydrate, fat or protein – but they can also measure how much of each is present.

The following three pages describe food tests that you can carry out in the school science laboratory. You can use them to detect the presence of sugars, starch, fats, proteins and vitamin C.

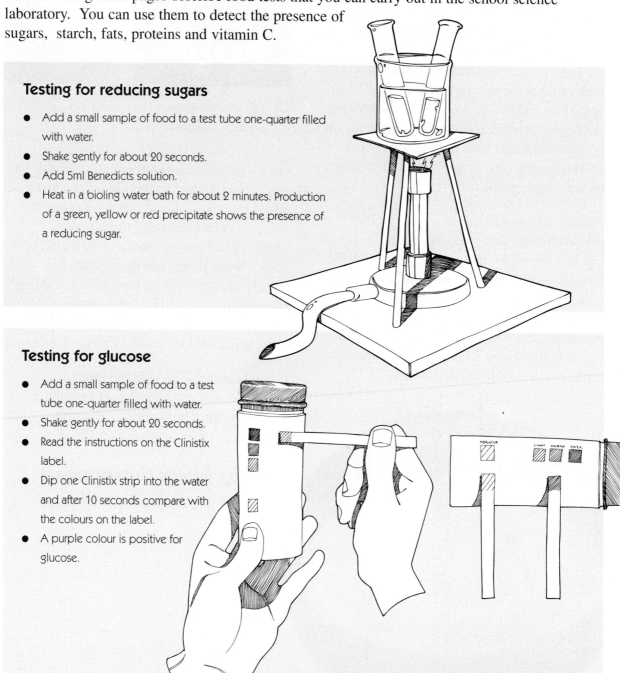

Testing for reducing sugars

- Add a small sample of food to a test tube one-quarter filled with water.
- Shake gently for about 20 seconds.
- Add 5ml Benedicts solution.
- Heat in a bioling water bath for about 2 minutes. Production of a green, yellow or red precipitate shows the presence of a reducing sugar.

Testing for glucose

- Add a small sample of food to a test tube one-quarter filled with water.
- Shake gently for about 20 seconds.
- Read the instructions on the Clinistix label.
- Dip one Clinistix strip into the water and after 10 seconds compare with the colours on the label.
- A purple colour is positive for glucose.

Testing for starch

- Add a small sample of food to a test tube one-quarter filled with water.
- Shake gently for about 20 seconds.
- Add two drops of iodine to the solution.
- A dark blue-black colour indicates the presence of starch.

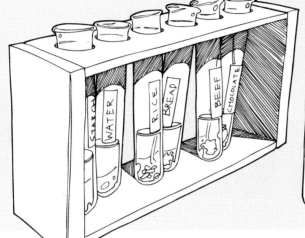

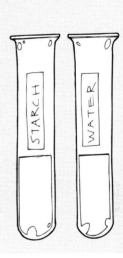

Testing for fat

- Place a sample of food in the middle of a piece of filter paper.
- Fold in half and press the food hard with the back of a clean teaspoon.
- Leave to dry in a warm place.
- Look at the dry filter papers against the light. A greasy spot indicates the presence of fat.

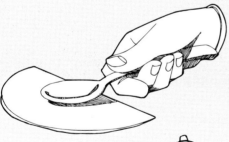

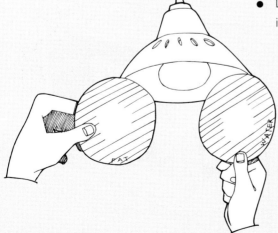

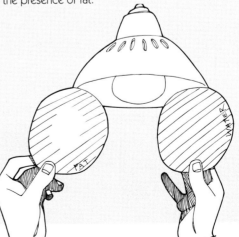

Testing for vitamin C

- Press a small sample of food onto a piece of DC PIP paper with the back of a clean teaspoon.
- If vitamin C is present the DCPIP will be colourized. Note that the pink colour mereky indicates the presence of a fruit acid not vitamin C.

Testing for protein

- Add a small sample of food to a test tube one-quarter filled with water.
- Shake gently for about 20 seconds.
- Add 8–10 drops of sodium hydroxide solution and leave to stand for 2 minutes.
- Now add 2–3 drops of copper sulphate solution and stir with a clear glass rod.
  Leave to stand for 10 minutes. A violet colour indicates the presence of protein.

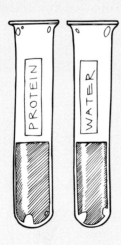

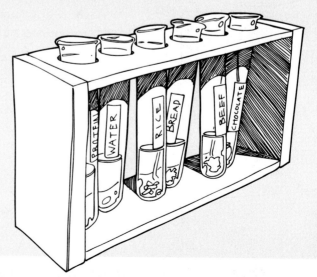

Digestion

The food you eat is broken down by your digestive system into a form which your body can use. This happens in various places in the body. **Enzymes** are produced by different parts of the body to break down the food into its component parts, as shown in the diagram.

	Food being digested	Enzymes used	Substances produced
Mouth	starch	salivary amylase	maltose
Stomach	protein	pepsin	polypeptides
Small Intestine	fat	lipase	fatty acids, glycerol
	starch	amylase	maltose
	protein & polypeptides	proteases	polypeptides & amino acids
	sucrose	sucrase	glucose & fructose
	maltose	maltase	glucose
	lactose	lactase	glucose & galactose

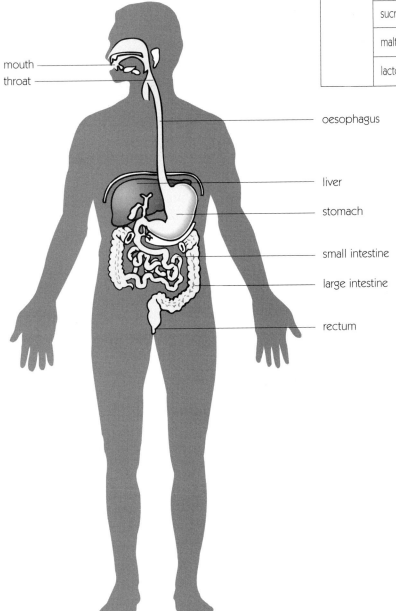

mouth

throat

oesophagus

liver

stomach

small intestine

large intestine

rectum

Role of dietary fibre

The remains of the food following digestion are made up mainly of dietary fibre, which moves into the large intestine. Dietary fibre is the name given to the insoluble non-starch polysaccharides (NSP) found in the cell walls of fruit, vegetables and cereals. It cannot be digested. Cellulose is an NSP, and bacteria living in the large intestine break down some of this to form B vitamins and vitamin K. Other NSPs that occur in plants are gums and lignius. Plants do contain soluble NSPs and most of these pass through the body without entering the blood system.

The most important function of dietary fibre is to hold water, rather like a sponge. This makes the faeces soft and bulky so they pass easily through the large intestine. The rate at which food passes through the body from the mouth to the anus is called the **transit time**. The transit time varies, but in the average person it is about 70 hours, and in the average vegetarian 43 hours. This is because the vegetarian diet is high in dietary fibre.

If the faeces do not contain a high proportion of dietary fibre, they will become small and hard. This makes the faeces difficult to pass out of the body. A person will feel uncomfortable and become constipated. If the muscles tighten into a painful spasm this is called irritable bowel syndrome. The wall of the large intestine can also develop weak points which will stretch into pouches (diverticula). Many elderly people suffer from diverticulitis when these pouches become inflamed. There is some evidence that a high-fibre diet will prevent large intestine cancer.

The average person eats 12 g of dietary fibre a day, and it is recommended that this is increased to 18 g per day. Sources of dietary fibre in the diet are shown in the table below. The main sources are bread and other cereal products, vegetables and fruit.

Food source	Fibre (g/100 g)
Meat	0.0
Baked beans	3.7
Beans, red kidney, boiled	6.7
Beans, runner, boiled	1.9
Cabbage, boiled	1.8
Carrots, boiled	2.5
Potatoes, boiled	1.2
Yams, boiled	1.4
Tomatoes, raw	1.0
Apples with skin, raw	1.8
Bananas	1.1
Raisins	2.0
Nuts, mixed	6.0
Biscuits, digestive	2.2
Biscuits, rich tea	1.7
Bread, white	1.5
Bread, brown	3.5
Bread, wholemeal	5.8
Flour, white	3.1
Flour, wholemeal	9.0
All Bran	24.5
Porridge oats	7.1
Rice Krispies	0.7
Shredded Wheat	9.8
Weetabix	9.7
Rice, white, boiled	0.1
Rice, brown, boiled	0.8
Spaghetti, white, boiled	1.2
Spaghetti, wholemeal, boiled	3.5

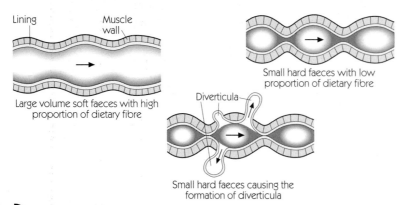

Lining   Muscle wall

Large volume soft faeces with high proportion of dietary fibre

Small hard faeces with low proportion of dietary fibre

Diverticula

Small hard faeces causing the formation of diverticula

The workings of the large intestine

Dietary needs

Food provides us with the nutrients that we need to live. It is the food choices that we make that affect our health. In order to help us make the right choices there is some general advice available.

The government has identified eight guidelines for a healthy diet:

- enjoy your food;
- eat a variety of different foods;
- eat the right amount to be a healthy weight;
- eat foods rich in starch and fibre;
- don't eat too much fat;
- don't eat sugary foods too often;
- look after the vitamins and minerals in your food;
- if you drink alcohol, keep within sensible limits.

To help us to follow these guidelines, *The Balance of Good Health* has been produced. This is a diagram of a plate divided up to show the proportions of groups of foods that a person should eat. By choosing food groups in the approximate proportions shown, and choosing different foods from within each group, a person is more likely to be healthy. Do not be misled by the plate. It is not necessary to eat all these foods in one meal. If the balance is achieved over a day or a week most people will be healthy.

The Balance of Good Health

Nutrients in food

These are summarized in the table below.

Nutrient	Function
carbohydrates	provide energy and can be converted into body fat
fats	provide a concentrated form of energy and can be converted into body fat
proteins	provide amino acids for growth and repair of body tissue. They can be converted into carbohydrate and used for energy
vitamins	help to regulate body processes
minerals	used in growth and repair and to help to regulate body processes

You can find out which foods are rich or poor in these nutrients by using the Chooser Charts on pages 152–155.

Water, like oxygen from the air, is essential for life, but it is not considered a food or a nutrient. Without water an adult can only survive for a few days. Every bodily process, both inside and outside the body cells, takes place in water.

Dietary fibre is the name given to a group of non-starch polysaccharides. It is found in wholegrain cereals, fruit and vegetables. Dietary fibre is not digested but it adds bulk to the faeces, helping the body to get rid of waste products (see page 142).

Nutritional information

This may be given in three ways.

1 Dietary Reference Values (DRVs)

These are guidelines as to the desirable intakes for particular food materials rather than estimates of individual requirements. They are average values for the population, consistent with good health. For example, the DRV for carbohydrate for adults is 47 per cent which means that 47 per cent of the daily energy intake should be provided by carbohydrate.

2 Reference Nutrient Intake (RNIs)

These give a daily amount of a nutrient that is enough for almost every individual, even those with high needs. For example, the RNI for protein for a 15–18-year-old female is 45 g.

3 Estimated Average Requirements for energy (EARs)

These give the daily average energy requirement for individuals of certain ages. So for a male of 15–18 years, this is 11.51 MJ (or 2755 kcal). Note that this is an average value; someone in this age group doing a large amount of manual work might require more than this, while someone whose work involves sitting down all day would need less.

Energy and obesity

Energy is obtained from carbohydrates, fats and protein. Energy is required for:

- physical activity;
- body processes such as breathing and heart beat;
- maintenance of body temperature.

The energy needed for body processes can be measured when a person is at complete rest or asleep. This is called the **basal metabolic rate (BMR)**. The BMR of a person is affected by:

- age – elderly people have a lower BMR than other adults;
- the amount of lean body tissue – men have a higher BMR than women.
- the person's state of health
- the climate

During pregnancy the BMR rises.

To maintain a healthy body weight, the amount of energy we take in from food should equal the energy output. In the UK, too many people are overweight or even obese. This is a form of malnutrition. These people are probably eating more foods which provide energy than are needed to balance their energy expenditure, so some of the carbohydrate, fat and protein is converted to body fat. This can happen even if the excess eaten is small. If it is consistently over the person's needs, the person will become overweight and then obese.

The graphs below give some idea of the range of weights for people of different heights. They can be used as a guide to tell you if a person is overweight.

Underweight
More food may be needed. In cases of very low weight a doctor should be consulted.

Correct
The right quantity of food is being eaten to maintain energy balance. If a person falls into the lower end of the weight range, they should maintain their weight and not be tempted to aim for the underweight category.

Overweight
Some loss of weight might be beneficial to health.

Obese
There is a need to lose weight.

Very obese
There is an urgent need to lose weight. It is advisable to consult a doctor or dietician.

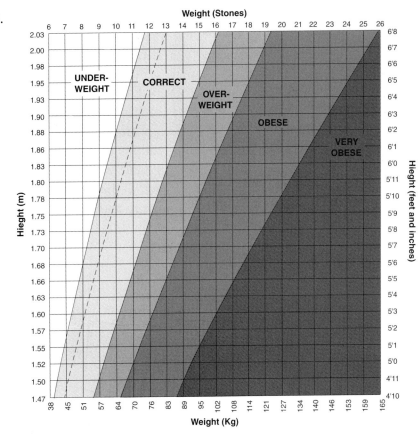

The energy provided by a food can be measured like this:

- 1 g dietary carbohydrate (sugar) provides 16 kJ or 4 kcal;

- 1 g dietary fat provides 37 kJ or 9 kcal;

- 1 g dietary protein provides 17 kJ or 4 kcal.

As you can see, each gram of fat provides twice as much energy as each gram of carbohydrate or protein.

It is easy to take in too much energy for two reasons.

1 Foods that provide the main sources of energy are readily available and eaten in quantity by most people – there is no shortage of bread, flour, meat, dairy produce or sugar.

2 Food products containing energy-dense ingredients are attractive, tasty and often seen as 'treats'. Fried foods, ice-cream, cakes and biscuits are all high in fat.

Foods which contain a high proportion of water such as fruit, salad vegetables and soup contain little protein, fat or carbohydrate and therefore little energy.

Weight can be lost by decreasing the amount of energy taken in, that is by decreasing the amount of high-energy foods eaten or by increasing physical activity. People vary, especially during adolescence when body shape is changing, so any weight-reducing diet should only be undertaken with the advice of a medical professional. Obese children tend to become obese adults unless, of course, they change their eating habits. People who are obese are more likely to develop diseases such as diabetes, cardiovascular disease, high blood pressure and certain cancers.

Coronary heart disease (CHD)

In the UK, coronary heart disease is a major health problem. It is one of the main causes of death. The risk of heart disease is increased by:

- smoking;
- high blood pressure;
- raised levels of cholesterol;
- obesity;
- a family history.

There is nothing you can do about your family history, but all the other factors, except smoking, are influenced by what you eat.

CHD is related to the amount and the type of fat in the diet. The foods with a high proportion of saturated fats include fatty meats, Cheddar cheese, sausages, beefburgers and butter. A diet high in saturated fats is also likely to be high in cholesterol. Cholesterol is a substance made in the liver and carried in the bloodstream. The cholesterol can build up and be deposited with other material as 'plaque' on the walls of the arteries, causing them to narrow. If the arteries then become blocked by a blood clot or more plaque, the person has a heart attack, which if severe can cause death.

The level of cholesterol in the blood depends on the amount of saturated fat in the diet. Replacing saturated fatty acids with unsaturated fatty acids can lower blood cholesterol. You can do this by using polyunsaturated fats and corn oil as alternatives to animal fat-based products. Note that some low-fat spreads contain animal fat. There is some concern about possible links between unsaturated fats and cancer. Note also that the soluble NSP pectin is thought to remove cholesterol from arteries.

The government recommends that, on average, the total fat content of a person's diet should not be more than 35 per cent, and the total saturated fatty acid content should not be more than 10 per cent.

These figures are lower than those for the average diet in the UK. In 1993, fat formed an average 40 per cent of the total energy intake, and the saturated fatty acid content was 16 per cent. So many people still need to be encouraged to reduce the fat and saturated fatty acid content of their diet.

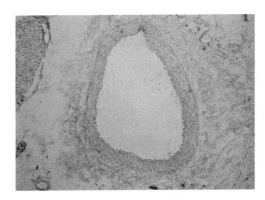

Corss section of a healthy artery; the blood can flow through freely

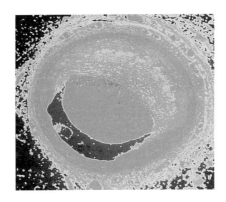

Cross section of an unhealthy artery which is almost blocked by a blood clot attached to the thickening of the artery wall, made from fibrous dead tissue, dead cells and cholesterol

8

Diabetes

Diabetes millitus is a disorder which reduces the ability of the body to control the amount of glucose in the blood. There are two forms of diabetes.

- Insulin-dependent diabetes (juvenile-onset diabetes) is a genetic abnormality that occurs around the ages of 10–12 years. It results when the body is unable to produce insulin because the cells in the pancreas are damaged or absent. The diabetic needs to have regular injections of insulin throughout life. The cause is not diet related.

- Late-onset diabetes occurs later in life and is often associated with obesity. It is due to the resistance of the body tissue to insulin. It does not require regular insulin injections and can often be controlled by diet. The diet aims to reduce the person's weight and to make sure that their rate of carbohydrate intake matches the available insulin.

All diabetics need to avoid large rises in blood glucose, which can result if they eat readily absorbed sugar, but this means controlling rather than reducing the total carbohydrate intake.

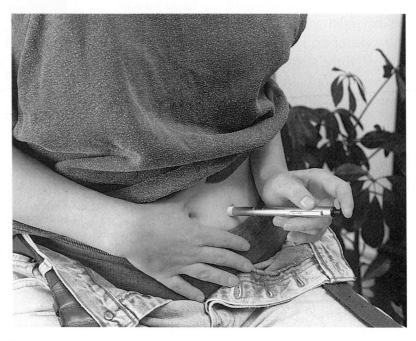

A diabetic injects herself with insulin before a meal

Bulimia nervosa and anorexia nervosa

These are serious eating disorders and are psychological conditions. People who suffer from them know a lot about food, especially weight-reducing diets, but need medical help to recover from their illness. The illness can be fatal.

A bulimia sufferer is concerned with their diet and weight. Food is an obsession, and they binge regularly. This means that they eat vast quantities of food, out of sight of other people. The food is not chewed properly but is stuffed into the mouth and swallowed quickly. These binges are then followed by self-induced bouts of vomiting and the use of laxatives. This can lead to physical damage as the gums and teeth become worn away by the action of the stomach acids and the voice becomes husky through persistent vomiting. Laxatives become necessary to prevent constipation, as the bowels are sore. Many bulimia sufferers feel guilty about their behaviour and become anxious and depressed. Bulimia sufferers are usually either within the normal weight range or above it.

People who suffer from anorexia avoid food and therefore lose weight. They become seriously underweight and look emaciated. They tend to become secretive and fear being discovered. They often pretend to eat and hide the food from other people, or they refuse to eat. They suppress their natural feelings of hunger and think that if they eat they will become fat. They think eating is a weakness, and that they are giving in to other people if they eat.

They use laxatives or make themselves vomit if they do eat anything. An anorexia sufferer may need medical attention to stay alive. Hospital treatment varies but always takes a long time. A combination of medical and psychiatric care is usually required.

People with bulimia and anorexia need help and support to change their eating habits. Like alcoholics, they first have to admit that there is a serious problem and then find the support they need to gain a more confident self-image. There are special programmes, including nutritional advice, to help sufferers change their self-destructive behaviour. Most important, though, is the help they need to uncover the root causes of the illness and to help them come to terms with them. This always takes a long time.

▶ *The distorting mirror reveals what this girl may think she really looks like. She believes she is too fat even though she is quite slim.*

Dental caries

Sugars and starches provide energy, but sugars, particularly when eaten frequently and in-between meals, are associated with increased tooth decay or **dental caries**. All carbohydrates can cause decay, but how much decay depends on:

- how often carbohydrate is eaten;
- the length of time it is in the mouth;
- the flow of saliva;
- the resistance of the teeth to decay;
- the presence of bacteria in the mouth and their ability to produce dental plaque.

Acid is formed in the mouth during the break down of carbohydrates by bacteria. This acid attacks the enamel on the teeth which begins to dissolve. After a while the saliva in the mouth will neutralize the acid and, if there is enough time, reverse the initial stages of decay. Some bacteria secrete a protective barrier (dental plaque) which sticks the bacteria to the teeth and protects them from the saliva. If more carbohydrate is eaten, the acid level in the mouth rises and the decay reaches a stage where it cannot be reversed and the tooth decay is permanent.

Sugar, in the form of sucrose, produces the necessary conditions for tooth decay, probably because we eat sugar so often. Starch, when eaten with sugar, also creates the conditions needed for decay. This may be because the starch helps to hold the sugar in the mouth giving the bacteria more time to produce acid. Fruit and vegetables contain sugar but do not tend to cause decay, though fruit juice, which has a higher concentration of sugar, does. Foods such as cheese and yoghurt are alkaline and therefore help neutralize the acid produced by the break down of carbohydrate. It is, therefore, better to finish a meal with one of these foods.

The government recommends that the amount of sugar from sucrose and fruit juice should contribute no more than 10 per cent to the energy content of the diet. In 1933, 13 per cent of the average person's food energy came from sugar and fruit juices. Since then, there has been an improvement in the dental health of the nation, though this is probably due to the use of fluoride toothpastes and fluoridation of the water supply rather than changes in diet.

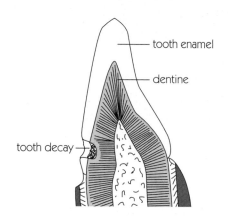

tooth enamel

dentine

tooth decay

Designing for nutrition

It is interesting to compare the traditional diets of different cultures. The pictures below compare typical meals from China and the UK. The first thing to notice is the overall balance of ingredients. The Chinese meal has lots of vegetables and a much smaller amount of fish or meat.

Rice:

carbohydrate (starch); B vitamins

Water chestnuts, peppers, onions, carrots, spring onions, bamboo shoots:

dietary fibre; iron; vitamins A, C

Stir-fry chicken:

protein; B vitamins

Cashew nuts:

protein; dietary fibre; sodium; calcium and iron

Sausages:

protein; fat; iron; calcium; sodium; B vitamins

Chips:

carbohydrate (starch); fat; dietary fibre; vitamin C

Peas:

carbohydrate (sugar and starch); dietary fibre; vitamin c

The UK meal usually has a much greater proportion of meat (unless, of course, it is a vegetarian meal). Sometimes the vegetables are little more than a 'garnish'. The way the food is cooked is different too. Deep-fat and shallow-fat frying are a popular way to cook food in the UK, while steaming and stir-frying are often used to cook traditional Chinese foods.

The complex range of food products available is changing the way we eat and altering traditional life styles.

Food product design

Nutrition Chooser Charts

You can use the information in these charts to make design decisions that meet nutrition specifications. For example, if a manufacturer requires a burger high in protein, iron and vitamin C but low in fat, you might trial a mixture of chicken, spinach and orange!

Food		Carbohydrate	Protein	Dietary fibre	Fat
	white flour	●●●●	●●	●●	●
	wholemeal flour	●●●●	●●●	●●●	●
	white pasta	●●●●	●●●		●
	wholemeal pasta	●●●●	●●●	●●●	●
	white rice	●●●●			
	wholegrain rice	●●●●		●●	●
	whole milk	●	●		●
	skimmed milk	●	●		
	natural yoghurt		●●		●
	Cheddar cheese		●●●●		●●●
	cottage cheese	●	●●●		●
	butter				●●●●
	sunflower oil				●●●●
	low-fat spread				●●
	eggs		●●●		●●
	chicken		●●●●		●
	rump steak		●●●●		●
	minced beef		●●●●		●●
	sausages	●	●●●		●●●
	bacon		●●●●		●●●

Key

The more ● the greater the amount of the nutrient present in the food.

NRT1
NRT2

Food	Minerals			Vitamins				
	sodium	calcium	iron	A	B	C	D	E
white flour	●	●●●	●●●		●●			
wholemeal flour	●	●●●	●●●	●	●			
white pasta		●			●			
wholemeal pasta		●			●			
white rice	●	●		●	●			
wholegrain rice				●●●				
whole milk	●	●●●		●●	●●●			
skimmed milk	●	●●●			●●●			
natural yoghurt		●●			●			
Cheddar cheese	●●●	●●●●		●●●●				
cottage cheese	●●	●●			●●●			
butter	●●●	●		●●●				
sunflower oil								●●●●
low-fat spread	●●●						●●●	●●●
eggs	●	●●	●●●	●●●	●●●●		●●●	●●
chicken	●	●	●●		●●			
rump steak	●	●	●●●		●●●			
minced beef	●	●	●●●		●●●			
sausages	●	●	●●●		●●●			
bacon	●●●●		●●●		●●●			

Key

The more ● the greater the amount of the nutrient present in the food.

Food product design

Food		Carbohydrate	Protein	Dietary fibre	Fat
	cod		●●●		
	sardines		●●●●		●●
	prawns		●●●●		●
	tuna		●●●●		●●
	Quorn®		●●●	●●	●
	cabbage		●	●●	
	broccoli	●	●●	●●	
	carrots	●	●	●●	
	boiled potato	●●●	●	●	
	spinach	●	●●	●●	●
	apple	●●	●	●●	
	avocado	●	●●	●●	●●
	banana	●●	●	●●	
	orange	●●	●	●●	
	melon	●	●	●	
	almonds	●	●●●	●●●●	●●●
	salted peanuts	●	●●●●	●●●	●●●
	walnuts	●	●●●	●●●	●●●
	sugar	●●●●			

Key

The more ● the greater the amount of the nutrient present in the food.

Food	Minerals			Vitamins				
	sodium	calcium	iron	A	B	C	D	E
cod	●	●	●		●●●			
sardines	●●●	●●●●	●●●		●●●●		●●●●	
prawns	●●●●	●●●	●●					
tuna	●●	●	●●●		●●●		●●●●	●●●●
Quorn®	●●		●		●●●			
cabbage	●	●	●	●●●●	●	●●●●		●
broccoli	●	●	●	●●●●	●●	●●●●		●●
carrots	●	●●	●	●●●●		●●		●
boiled potato	●	●	●		●	●●	●	
spinach	●●	●●●	●●●	●●●●	●●●	●●●●		●●●
apple	●	●		●	●●	●		
avocado	●	●	●●●	●	●●●	●●●●		●●●
banana	●	●	●	●●●	●	●●●		
orange	●		●	●●	●	●●●●		
melon	●	●	●	●●●		●●●●		●
almonds	●	●●●	●●●●		●●●			●●●●
salted peanuts	●●●	●●	●●●		●●●●			●●●●
walnuts	●	●●	●●●		●●●			●
sugar		●						

Key

The more ● the greater the amount of the nutrient present in the food.

Food product design

You can present the nutritional information about any of the food materials in the Chooser Charts as pie charts, as shown here. This makes it a lot easier to compare the nutrition of different foods.

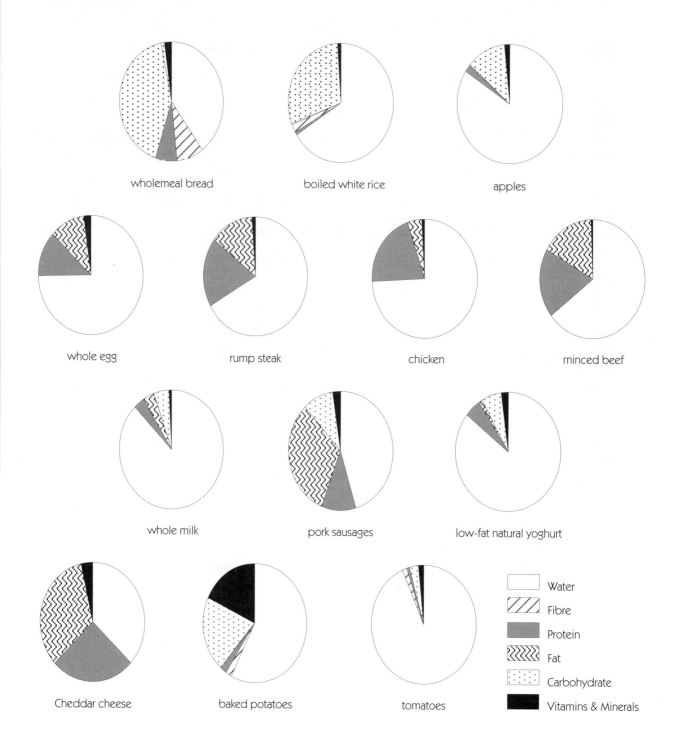

wholemeal bread

boiled white rice

apples

whole egg

rump steak

chicken

minced beef

whole milk

pork sausages

low-fat natural yoghurt

Cheddar cheese

baked potatoes

tomatoes

Water

Fibre

Protein

Fat

Carbohydrate

Vitamins & Minerals

Nutritional content of foods (as percentage of total weight)

How cooking methods affect nutrition

The way you choose to cook foods can make a big difference to the nutritional quality.

Putting food into hot fat or oil is a very quick and tasty way to cook it. When you fry food in this way you add dietary energy in the form of fat. Just how much you add depends on the style of frying you use, as shown here. One way to reduce the absorption of fat during frying is to make sure that the fat is very hot before you put the food in. This way the outside of the food is sealed and prevents too much fat from being absorbed.

Low- and high-fat potatoes

Most fat absorbed – Least fat absorbed

Grilling and roasting are ways of cooking without adding any fat although some foods, like white fish, need to be brushed lightly with oil.

Cooking food in water or steam does not add fat but it can destroy vitamin C and thiamin (one of the B vitamins). Green vegetables can still be good sources of these vitamins if you cook them carefully. Microwaving vegetables uses only a tiny amount of water and is fast so there is little vitamin loss.

Boiling/steaming   Steaming   Micro-waving

Greatest vitamin loss – Least vitamin loss

Designing for flavour and odour

When you eat, the taste buds in your tongue detect four basic types of taste. These are sweet, bitter, sour and salty. The numerous combinations of these means that you can taste a huge range of flavours.

While you are eating, your nose and mouth senses work together to tell you the flavour of the food. Sometimes you can guess what a food will taste like just by smelling it, and if you hold your nose (or when you have a cold) the taste of the food can be affected. The senses of smell and taste can therefore be seen to be interlinked.

Below are some examples of how you could describe the taste or odour of a product. Flavours and odours can also be described by the names of the main ingredients.

For example, a burger might be described as 'very beefy' or having a 'meaty taste'. Both these examples use the character of the food to help describe its taste or smell.

You can also describe the taste/smell in terms of its intensity. For example, this could range from 'strong', 'powerful' or 'pungent' to 'medium', 'weak' or 'mild', ending with 'subtle', 'faint' or 'bland'.

How far can you go?

This chart shows eight different products. For each one it is possible to have a range of different intensities of flavour and odour. When you design, you will need to decide which ingredients you want to give the product its overall flavour and odour.

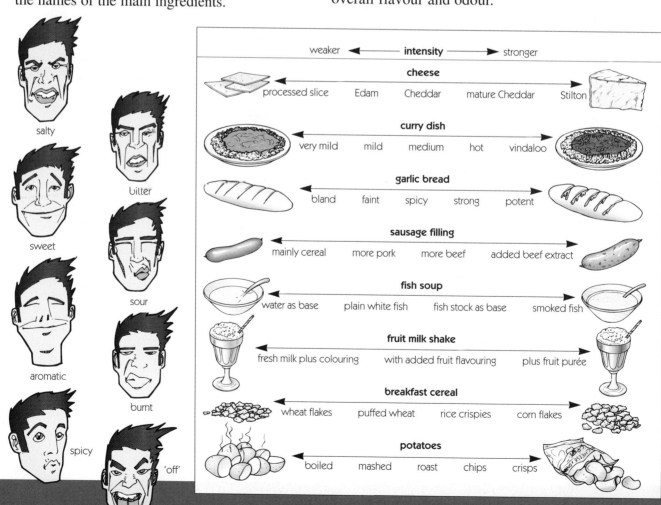

	weaker ◄——— intensity ———► stronger			
cheese	processed slice	Edam	Cheddar	mature Cheddar	Stilton
curry dish	very mild	mild	medium	hot	vindaloo
garlic bread	bland	faint	spicy	strong	potent
sausage filling	mainly cereal	more pork	more beef	added beef extract	
fish soup	water as base	plain white fish	fish stock as base	smoked fish	
fruit milk shake	fresh milk plus colouring	with added fruit flavouring	plus fruit purée		
breakfast cereal	wheat flakes	puffed wheat	rice crispies	corn flakes	
potatoes	boiled	mashed	roast	chips	crisps

salty

bitter

sweet

sour

aromatic

burnt

spicy

'off'

What gives a food product a particular smell or flavour?

The ingredients

Each ingredient has its own unique flavour and odour. The effect this has on the smell and flavour of a food product is determined by the following.

- *Amount used* – one of the most important factors in determining its final taste, e.g. some spices are extremely potent so only small quantities are needed; others are needed in large amounts to impart their flavour or odour.

- *Age* – the age of an ingredient can alter its taste and smell quite dramatically. Some cheeses are matured for 6–9 months so that the flavour/odour can develop. Fruit is left to ripen so that it is acceptable to eat. The age of an animal when it is slaughtered also has an effect on taste, e.g. mutton has a different taste from lamb.

- *Processing method* – can affect flavour/odour, e.g. bacteria used to produce yoghurt from milk give it its characteristic flavour/odour. Flour can also have different types of flavours depending on the processing; plain, wholemeal and granary flours give different-tasting breads.

- *Handling* – some ingredients are easily damaged; they bruise and become contaminated with bacteria which affects the flavour/odour.

- *Additional flavourings* – some ingredients have extra flavourings added to them, such as vanilla-flavoured sugar.

Preservation techniques

- *Smoking* – gives a characteristic smoky flavour and odour, e.g. herring are smoked and sold as kippers.

- *Pickling* – the ingredients taste sharp due to the presence of vinegar.

- *Jam-making* – ingredients become extremely sweet, due to the high sugar content.

- *Dehydration* – the foods may loose some of their flavour and odour.

Pre-cooking and storage

- *Cross-contamination of flavours/odours* – some ingredients have a very strong flavour and odour which can be indirectly absorbed by other ingredients if they are not correctly wrapped and stored.

- *Marinades* – a mixture of strong flavours is poured over an ingredient, usually meat, to add extra flavour.

Cooking techniques

- *Microwaving* – may leave the food with a bland flavour (see baking/grilling below).

- *Boiling* – this may draw out the flavouring/smells into the water as some are water soluble.

- *Grilling* – this causes the starch in the product to go brown. This process is called dextrinization. A good example is toast.

- *Baking and roasting* – this develops flavour/odour through a variety of processes including dextrinization, caramelization and the Maillard reaction (see page 135).

- *Frying* – fried foods are tasty because some flavours and odours are fat soluble.

Food product design

Getting it right

The table summarizes all the areas that are important in giving a food product the desired smell and flavour. It is important to get all of these right at the same time. The correct ingredients can be spoiled by:

- using too much or too little;
- sloppy preparation;
- bad cooking.

Selecting the ingredient	Weighing and measuring	Careful preparation	Cooking
make sure the ingredients are appropriate	careful weighing	personal hygiene	before cooking, marinade perhaps
	careful measuring	careful handling	correct cooking method …
	get the intensity right	avoid contamination	for the right time

Testing and tasting

The proof of the pudding is in the eating! It is easy to measure and weigh the right amount of a flavouring to go in a product, but the crucial factors are the final taste and smell. You will need to use the food product evaluation techniques described in the *Strategies* section (pages 92–96) to record people's opinions on the flavour and odour of your product. Controlled tests need to be devised and clear, accurate records kept of the results which later can be used to evaluate the product and to help you make design decisions to improve it.

Here are some suggestions as to how the smell and flavour of different food products might be enhanced:

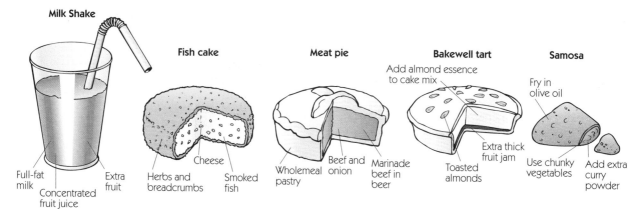

Milk Shake — Full-fat milk, Concentrated fruit juice, Extra fruit

Fish cake — Herbs and breadcrumbs, Cheese, Smoked fish

Meat pie — Wholemeal pastry, Beef and onion, Marinade beef in beer

Bakewell tart — Add almond essence to cake mix, Extra thick fruit jam, Toasted almonds

Samosa — Fry in olive oil, Use chunky vegetables, Add extra curry powder

Flavour/Odour Additives Chooser Chart

You can use this chart to help you make design decisions to get the flavour and smell needed.

Additive	Typical uses		Other considerations
Herbs: basil garlic mint sage coriander cumin	soups casseroles chicken kiev stuffing	stews garlic bread sausages sauces (mint sauce, pesto)	Herbs change the appearance of the product slightly by leaving coloured flecks. Can be cut into small pieces and blended, sprinkled or layered.
Spices: allspice clove cinnamon curry chilli saffron vanilla cardamom garam masala	Can be used in both sweet and savoury products: apple pies Indian dishes tacos ice-cream	toppings chilli con carne rice dishes confectionery	Colour changes may occur, e.g. saffron and curry powder cause a yellow colour. Fresh spices may be able to be chopped or crushed into products (like herbs). Some are used whole, like cloves, leaving a visual and textural change.
Sauces: mint soy Tabasco pesto Worcester sorito tomato ketchup	To enhance the flavour and to complement the main product. A dash in soups, stews, gravies, meat/fish dishes or in a stir-fry.		The sauce may alter the overall colour of a product. It can also add another colour if used as an accompaniment. They are runny so can be added easily.
Enhancers: monosodium glutamate	Help to bring out the flavour of the food, such as meat and fish – used mainly in Chinese cooking.		There has been some concern that this can exacerbate hyperactivity.
Extracts: beef extract (Bovril) yeast extract (Marmite)	Can be added to soups, stews, casseroles and gravies. Used as a spread or a drink.		Can alter the overall colour of the product. If using meat extracts check acceptability. Pastes can be spread, layered or dissolved in another liquid.
Condiments: salt pepper vinegar mustard	Used as overall flavour/odour enhancers. Salt can reduce sourness of an acidic product. Pepper can give an aromatic smell. Mustard can be used in sauces and in a relish.		These can change the appearance of the product slightly by leaving coloured flecks or altering the overall colour. Too much vinegar can cause the product to go soggy. Some mustards are smooth, others are grainy.
Essential oils/essences: allspice oil liquid annatto	Essential oils are pure extracts obtained from fruits and other plants. They are very expensive. Artificial/synthetic versions are available. Added to confectionery, bakery items, ice-creams.		Taste of artificial flavourings may not be perfect. However, their use may be based on economic considerations. Some artificial flavourings may behave inconsistently at high temperatures.

Designing for colour

Is the colour of food important? Imagine a world where everything was black, white and grey!

 Colour is important for food

Our first impression of food is visual, so the colour of food is important. Food colour can tell us what flavour to expect – we can assume that the red liquid in the bowl is tomato soup.

We associate certain colours with certain foods – if the colour is unfamiliar we are quite likely to reject the food even though the flavour is probably just the same. The colour of food can also tell us about its condition. You can tell just by looking at bananas which ones arc ready to eat, which ones should be left a while and which ones should be thrown away.

 Only one of these foods looks palatable

Controlling colour

You can control the colour of food products by:

- adding coloured ingredients;
- adding food colourings;
- the choice of ingredients;
- the method of cooking;
- the temperature at which the food is cooked;
- the length of time you cook it.

Adding coloured ingredients

Coloured ingredients alter the flavour of foods as well.

Using coloured ingredients to add spots of colour.

Using coloured ingredients to add colour to the surface of solids.

Using food colourings

Food colours do not alter the flavour of foods. You can use them to produce a range of colours from very pale to very dark, as shown here. When you design you will need to think about which colours will be acceptable to consumers.

Red food colouring was used to provide this range of colours

Choice of ingredients

The choice of ingredients can alter the colour of foods, for example:

- white or golden castor sugar in a Victoria sponge sandwich;
- white or wholemeal flour in bread;
- white fat or butter in pastry.

Note that the choice of ingredients will often affect the nutritional value of the product as well (see page 151).

Using coloured ingredients to give an overall colour.

Cooking method

When food is grilled or baked it turns brown, due to dextrinization, caramelization and the Maillard reaction. The colour changes very little when food is steamed or microwaved.

Time and temperature

You can control the colour of food by the temperature you choose to cook it at and for how long. If you cook a cereal-based food, for example a cake, at a low temperature for a short time it will be pale in colour. If you cook it for a longer time it will become slightly darker. You can also make it a darker colour by cooking it at a higher temperature, but you must be careful not to cook it for too long as it could burn. The panel below shows the effects of cooking temperature and times on a Victoria sponge sandwich cake.

(1) Microwaving

(2) Steaming

(3) Roasting

(4) Frying

(a) 190°C, 20 mins   (b) 190°C, 30 mins

(c) 220°C, 20 mins   (d) 220°C, 30 mins

Preventing colour changes

Sometimes you need to prevent colour changes because they can spoil the appearance of food, for example apples and bananas go brown very quickly in the presence of oxygen. The modified atmosphere in some salad packaging contains less oxygen and more nitrogen than ordinary air. This reduces the speed of oxygen-dependent colour changes so the lettuce leaves, for example, don't go brown so quickly.

Getting food products the same colour every time

Food producers have to make sure their products always look the same, as this is what consumers expect.

Foods often change colour when they are processed. During canning, the colour of peas changes to a rather unappealing grey-green due to the break down of the chlorophyll in the peas. The producer uses a permitted food colouring to return the food to its natural colour after processing, so that every batch looks the same.

We expect every McDonald's burger bun to be the same golden colour. This does not happen by chance. Every fifteen minutes a quality assurance checker takes a burger bun from the production line and compares it with a colour photograph of the product to see whether it is the correct colour. If the colour is different, adjustments are made to either the temperature or the cooking time to bring the colour back to what it should be.

If the products you design and make have to meet these sorts of requirements, then you will need to keep accurate notes of ingredients, quantities, processing methods, cooking times and temperatures. In this way you will be able to reproduce the conditions needed to get the product 'just right' every time. And, just as important, you will be able to give precise instructions that enable others to achieve this too.

Each one the same colour every time!

Designing for texture

The texture of a product is what the food feels like in the mouth. Another name for texture is **mouthfeel**.

As you eat a food, its texture changes. The process of chewing breaks down its structure so that it is easy to swallow. When you bite into a biscuit the immediate mouthfeel may be crisp, followed by crunchy as you start to chew. As you continue chewing the structure breaks down further and saliva in the mouth causes the biscuit to become much softer. Finally, after the biscuit has been chewed and mixed with saliva the final mouthfeel may be slightly grainy and gooey.

Below are some examples of how you could describe the texture of a product.

Textures can also be described by the names of the ingredients themselves. For example, a fruit and nut cake might be described as having a nutty or crunchy texture. This example uses the character of the food to help describe it.

You can also describe the texture in terms of its intensity. For example, this could range from 'hard' through 'crisp', 'crunchy', 'crumbly', 'chewy', 'gooey,' 'creamy' and eventually to 'soft'.

How far can you go?

This chart shows eight different products. For each one it is possible to have a range of different intensities of texture. When you design, you will need to decide which ingredients you want to give the product its final overall mouthfeel.

soft

creamy

gooey

chewy

crumbly

crunchy

crisp

hard

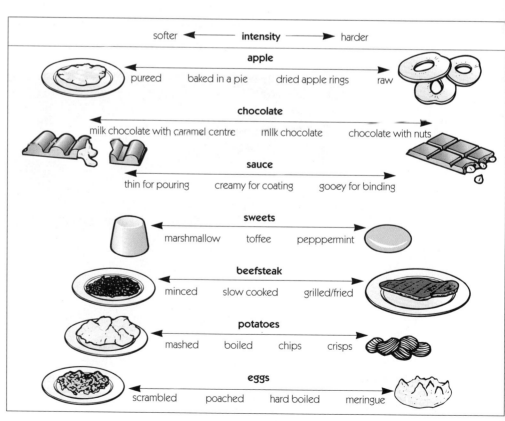

softer ← **intensity** → harder

apple
pureed   baked in a pie   dried apple rings   raw

chocolate
milk chocolate with caramel centre   milk chocolate   chocolate with nuts

sauce
thin for pouring   creamy for coating   gooey for binding

sweets
marshmallow   toffee   pepppermint

beefsteak
minced   slow cooked   grilled/fried

potatoes
mashed   boiled   chips   crisps

eggs
scrambled   poached   hard boiled   meringue

What gives a food product a particular texture?

The ingredients

Each ingredient has its own unique texture. The effect this has on the texture of a food product is determined by the following.

- *Amount used* – how much or how little of an ingredient you use in a product is one of the most important factors in controlling texture. Too little flour in a sauce will result in a watery consistency; too much and it might become so thick it cannot be poured!

- *Age of the ingredient* – in certain foods, this can affect texture enormously. In fruits and vegetables, for example, the texture changes as they age due to ripening.

Mechanical treatment

During the preparation of a food, many different physical actions can affect its texture. The more mechanical treatment it receives the more tender the food material will become. A range of mechanical treatments affecting texture are summarized below.

Pounding

Slicing

Cutting

Chopping

Mincing

Grating

Puréeing

Whisking

Chemical treatment

A range of substances can affect the texture of a food product through chemical reactions.

- Tenderizing – dilute acid, often in the form of vinegar or citrus fruit juice, breaks down the protein structures in meat in a marinade.

- Foaming – the reaction of sodium bicarbonate to heat or weak acids such as cream of tartar causes carbon dioxide to form, making mixes and doughs rise. Baking powder is a commercially prepared mixture of these ingredients. The growth of yeasts in bread dough causes carbon dioxide to be released making the dough rise.

- Setting – the presence of pectin, a carbohydrate, causes jams to set. The presence of gelatin, a protein, causes jellies to set.

Cooking techniques

The way you cook the food product will affect its texture. Different cooking methods result in different textures. Here are some examples.

- Frying in oil (which is fast) gives crispness.
- Casseroling (long, slow, sealed heating) tenderizes tough meat and vegetables.
- Grilling (which is fast) gives a crisp outer coating and a cooked, tender inside.
- Boiling in water causes vegetables to become tender but egg white to go hard.

Food product design

Texture Chooser Chart: Ingredients

You can use this Chooser Chart to help you decide on how to get the texture you want from the main ingredients you are using.

Ingredient	Mechanical treatments	Chemical treatments	Cooking methods
meat	pound slice cut mince	use marinades to tenderize	casseroling for tough cuts roasting for joints grilling for thin slices frying for mince
fish	slice cut	use marinades to tenderize	poaching frying grilling
cheese	slice grate		suitable for melting or mixing into fillings
eggs	whisking egg whites gives foam		scrambling poaching boiling frying
fruit	slice chop purée	use pectin to produce jams	boiling baking
vegetables	slice chop grate purée		boiling baking steaming casseroling
sugar			boiling sugar solutions first gives syrups and finally caramel

Note that for many of the conventional cooking methods there are microwave oven equivalents.

Texture Chooser Chart: Flour-based products

You can use this Chooser Chart to help you get the texture you want for pasta, breads, pastries and cakes.

Product	Critical ingredients	Mechanical treatments	Cooking methods	Possible additions
pasta	type of flour	different extrusions possible	boil in water until soft enough to eat easy to overcook	
breads	type of flour raising agent	knead to make dough elastic or use vitamin C as short-time method	bake until crust hard but inside soft	seeds and nuts on top for crunchiness dried fruit inside for gooiness
pastries	type of flour ratio of fat to flour	shortcrust – roll out for crumbliness flaky – roll and fold for crispness	bake – timing crucial; edges easily burned steam fry	fresh and dried fruit for gooiness sugar for graininess nuts for crunchiness
cakes	type of flour raising agent sugar ratio of fat to flour	rubbing in for crumbly/chewy creaming for chewy/gooey whisking for soft/creamy melting for chewy/crumbly	bake – timing crucial; edges easily burned steam microwave – no crispness	dried fruit for gooiness nuts for crunchiness chocolate chip for crunchiness followed by smoothness

Texture Chooser Chart: Sauces

You can use this Chooser Chart to help you get the texture you want for sauces.

Sauce	Critical ingredients	Mechanical treatments	Cooking methods	Possible additions
sweet sauces, e.g. custard	proportion of starch to liquid		stir during heating; starch mixtures must boil	
savoury sauces, e.g. cheese sauce	proportion of starch to liquid		stir during heating; starch mixtures must boil for gravy stir starch into meat juices	mushrooms for chewiness hard-boiled egg for crumbliness
fruit sauces	proportion of fruit to liquid	sieve or purée in liquidizer and then sieve to remove pips and stones	steam, simmer or microwave to soften	pieces of raw fruit for crunchiness
vegetable sauces, e.g. tomato sauce	proportion of vegetable to liquid	sieve or purée in liquidizer and then sieve to remove pips	steam, simmer or microwave to soften	onion for crunchiness

Food product design

Designing for finish

Your first impression of food is often what it looks like, so the final appearance of a food product is important. It needs to be attractive to those who are going to buy it or eat it. You can see the importance of good assembly and good finishing in this pizza.

You need to think about how to make food products look good:

- as you assemble them;
- when you cook them;
- as you add the finishing touches just before you serve them.

Examples of all three techniques used to good effect are shown opposite.

Good assembly

Good cooking

Good finishing touches

Getting the right shape

You can use the following techniques to achieve different shapes for food products.

Careful folding of food used as wrapping

Extrusion

Using ready-shaped containers

Using ready-shaped moulds

Careful free cutting with a knife

Using a ready-shaped cutter

Food product design

Controlling surface colour

You can use the following techniques to achieve different surface colours for food products.

1. Using a glaze to get a shiny surface

2. Using high temperature to get a browned surface

3. Applying a coloured finish

Controlling surface texture

You can use the following techniques to achieve different surface textures on food products.

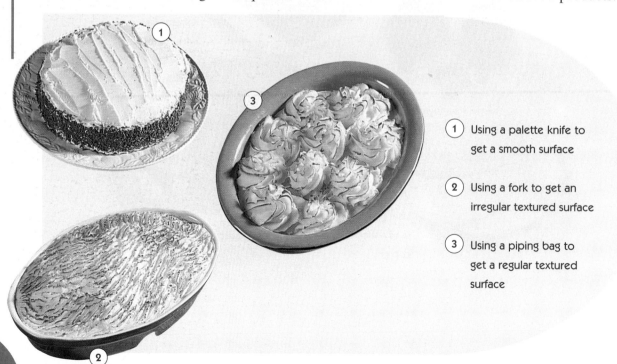

1. Using a palette knife to get a smooth surface

2. Using a fork to get an irregular textured surface

3. Using a piping bag to get a regular textured surface

Adding a garnish

A garnish is a good way to enhance the appearance of a food product. At the same time a garnish often complements the flavour and character of the product, for example a pastry fish shape used to garnish a fish pie. Garnishes can take quite a long time to prepare so you need to build this into your preparation time. You may also need to find time to practise some of the skilled techniques for producing garnishes. The Japanese in particular have made an art of simple and stunning food garnishes – we can learn from them that the simplest garnishes are often the most effective.

You can use the following garnishings to improve the appearance of the products you design and make.

Putting the finishing techniques onto the packaging

If you need to develop packaging for the food products you design and make, you may need to use all the finishing techniques described in this section to provide a photograph of your product within a serving suggestion. It will need to be well finished, well garnished and well presented.

Designing for the shelf-life of a product

Why is it important?

When plants are harvested or animals slaughtered, they start to deteriorate. Cells inside the food break down and become vulnerable to micro-organisms. This in turn starts changes in shape, colour, odour, flavour and texture. It is therefore extremely important that this process is delayed so that products, once manufactured, do not deteriorate and are in a fit state to sell.

The shelf-life is the time a product can spend 'on the shelf' before it is sold. Food products that exceed their shelf-life have to be thrown away. Means of prolonging shelf-life are summarized in the table below.

Means of prolonging shelf-life	Comments
Ingredient selection	The fresher the ingredients the longer they last.
Hygienic practice	Poor practice leads to contamination that reduces shelf-life.
Cooking process	Cooked foods sometimes have longer shelf-lives than raw foods.
Preservation techniques: ● low temperature	 Chilling (5°C) slows down micro-organism growth. Freezing (-18°C) stops micro-organisms growing. Can affect texture.
● high temperature	High temperatures kill micro-organisms; super-heated steam needed to kill the most resistant.
● dehydration	Removes the water from the food, killing the micro-organisms at the same time. Affects both taste and texture.
● pickling	The presence of dilute acid (vinegar) prevents the growth of micro-organisms. Affects taste and texture.
● jamming	The presence of sugar in high concentration kills the micro-organisms. Affects both taste and texture.
● smoking	The chemicals in the smoke prevent growth of micro-organisms. Affects both taste and texture.
● salting	Kills micro-organisms and prevents their growth. Modern salting uses nitrites and is less effective than traditional salting. Affects both taste and texture.
● irradiation	Kills micro-organisms and has little effect on taste or texture.
Selective breeding	Strains that stay fresh longer can be encouraged.
Gene manipulation	In the early stages of development.
Packaging: ● vacuum packaging	 Removes air and so prevents micro-organism growth.
● modified atmosphere packaging	Prevents enzyme action, moisture loss and micro-organism growth.
● canning/bottling	Uses high temperature sterilization and prevents further contamination.
● wrappers	Protect from pest and physical damage and prevent product from drying out. Some products need permeable wrappers to prevent condensation, which can encourage growth of micro-organisms.
Proper storage: ● cool, clean and dry	 For dried goods.
● chill, clean and dry	For refrigerated goods.
● cold, clean and dry	For frozen goods.

The effects of extending shelf-life

It is important to think about the effects that processing might have on the food products you have designed and made. It is one thing to produce an acceptable prototype product; it is another to ensure that it can be processed to extend its shelf-life and still be acceptable to the consumer. In this section you will consider the effects of three ways of extending shelf-life – canning, freezing and drying.

Canning

In commercial canning the food product is placed into a can, then ensuring that all the air is removed, the can is sealed, heated to a temperature of 121°C, held at that temperature for the required time then cooled and labelled. The heating process kills virtually all micro-organisms and most spores that would be capable of growth during storage. During heating the can is rotated to distribute the heat evenly so that there are no hot spots or cold spots. The water used to cool the can is chlorinated as sometimes tiny amounts can enter the can through a seam that leaks at high temperatures. Chlorinated water is sterile and will not contaminate the food.

The heat treatment is quite severe and may well alter both the appearance and taste of the food product being canned. Chemicals that give the product its natural colouring may be broken down. Tinned peas contain an added green dye because otherwise they would appear grey!

If you have produced a food product that might be canned you will need to think about how the canning process will affect it and how you might minimize these effects.

Here are some guidelines.

- Cut food into small pieces for ease of handling and to avoid air pockets.
- Avoid over-small pieces that break down into a mush.
- Blanch fruit and vegetables to prevent enzymic browning reactions.
- Use heat-resistant permitted colourings.

You can investigate the effect of the canning process on food products you have designed and made by heating them in a pressure cooker.

What processing allowed these food materials to be canned?

Freezing

Freezing extends the shelf-life of a food product because low temperatures slow down the growth of micro-organisms and the action of enzymes. The production of ice during freezing causes water to be withdrawn from the food and this dehydration also prevents the growth of micro-organisms.

The freezing cycle of a food is summarized in the diagram below. It is important for the thermal arrest time to be as short as possible. In plant materials a long thermal arrest time leads to the formation of large ice crystals from water drawn out of the cells, causing dehydration. On thawing the cells will be in a collapsed state and there will be a lot of water outside the cells, giving the product a watery texture.

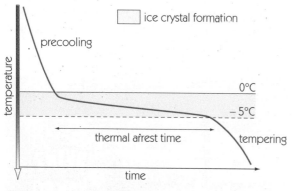

Freezing cycle of food

If you have produced a food product that might be frozen you will need to think about how the freezing process will affect it and how you might minimize these effects. Here are some guidelines.

- Choose ingredients that are known to freeze well
- Freeze the product as quickly as possible.

You can investigate the effect of the freezing process on food products you have designed and made by putting them in a freezer. You can increase the speed of freezing by using a small, battery-powered, hand-held fan to blow cold air around the product while it is in the freezer. Alternatively, your teacher may be able to find a supply of liquid nitrogen which can be used for very rapid freezing. Take care, it is very cold ($-196°C$) and causes severe cold burns.

Instant coffee is made by accelerated freeze drying

Drying

Drying extends the shelf-life of a food product because a lack of water prevents micro-organisms from growing. The removal of water causes the food to shrink in size, but as water evaporates from the surface this becomes dried out and rigid first, fixing the shape of the food early in the drying process. Rapid drying is best, giving a light honeycomb internal structure that is easy to rehydrate. However, if too much heat is applied to achieve this drying then the surface 'case hardens' which slows dehydration and prevents rehydration.

It is possible to achieve drying without heating by **freeze drying**. This process is carried out by freezing the product and then putting it under a strong vacuum. Instead of the ice melting it sublimes to leave the product in a dry state. There is a little shrinkage, little flavour change, no case hardening and good rehydration. The resulting product is very fragile; the honeycomb structure crumbles readily if not handled carefully. For this process to be economical in industry, the frozen product is heated very gently as the vacuum is applied. This is known as accelerated freeze drying (AFD).

Designing for cost

Value for money?

Consumers want good value for money and like prices to be as low as possible because they only have a limited amount of money to spend on food. Food manufacturers and retailers need prices to be as high as possible so that they can invest back into the business and make a profit. Making a food product for yourself often seems cheaper than buying it ready-made. Here is an example:

Sainsbury's apple pie costs £1.79

500g apples costs 39p

200g flour cost 4p

Tin of pie filling costs 59p

Packet of pastry costs 45p

100g margarine costs 10p

75g sugar costs 5p

Food product design

The ready-to-eat pie costs three times as much as one you make yourself from raw ingredients, even though the ingredients are probably almost the same. So why are the costs different? Here are some possibilities.

Processing the product

In the ready-to-eat pie the ingredients have been prepared, cooked, assembled and finished. All you have to do is take it out of the packaging and put it in the oven.

With the pie filling and ready-prepared pastry, the ingredients have been prepared but not cooked, assembled or finished. You have to open the tins, roll out the pastry, assemble the filling and pastry in a dish and then bake.

With the raw ingredients you have to do everything yourself – preparation, cooking, assembling and finishing. For the pastry you have to weigh out the ingredients, mix and roll out. You have to peel, core and slice the apples. You then have to assemble the filling and pastry in a dish and then bake.

The more processing there is in a food product, the more you have to pay for it but the less you have to do.

Packaging the product

The ready-to-eat pie is fragile and needs to be packaged carefully to prevent it being damaged during transport and while it is on the supermarket shelf.

The pie filling is in a tin and the ready-prepared pastry is in a packet.

The ingredients for the home-made pie are wrapped in paper; the apples may not be packaged at all.

The more packaging there is around a food product the more you have to pay for it.

Is it worth the price?

It is almost impossible for a food manufacturer to produce a fruit pie that is as good as one that has been freshly baked at home. But there is a high cost in terms of the time and effort that must be put in to producing the home-baked pie. If people are very busy and the choice is between a ready-to-eat pie and no pie at all, then clearly a ready-to-eat pie is value for money. Note also that any one brand of mass-produced ready-to-eat pies will be reliable in that the pies will always be of the same quality. But this reliability is only achieved by using certain sorts of materials in the product. It will contain a wide range of additives (see page 208); the pastry is likely to be high in fat and the filling high in sugar.

Keeping costs low at home

There are a variety of ways to reduce the cost of a food product. The example here shows how you can do this for a food product you might prepare at home. You can use the information to calculate the maximum saving you could make when adapting the recipe for a fish pie. Note that by changing the ingredients to lessen the cost, you will change both the taste and the nutrition of the product.

1 Decrease the amount of expensive ingredient and make up the difference with a cheaper but similar ingredient, e.g. use half tuna and half haddock.
Saves 32p

2 Change main ingredient for a less expensive one, e.g. use all tuna instead of haddock.
Saves 63p

3 Decrease the amount of expensive ingredients and make up the difference with cheaper, different indregients, e.g. use sweetcorn, mushrooms and (or) red pepper instead of some of the fish.
Saves 44p

4 Decrease the amount of expensive filling and increase the amount of less-expensive topping, e.g. reduce the amount of fish plus sauce and increase the amount of potato topping.
Saves 40p

5 Increase the amount of sauce and decrease the amount of filling.
Saves 56p

Keeping costs low in industry

Food manufacturers carry out similar cost-cutting exercises, as shown here.

1 Decrease the amount of expensive ingredients and make up the difference with a cheaper but similar ingredient,
  e.g. use half pork and half beef.

2 Use less ingredients per burger by changing the size of the burger,
  e.g. make it thinner or of smaller diameter.

3 Decrease the amount of expensive ingredients and make up the difference with cheaper, different ingredients,
  e.g. use less beef and more rusk but add flavouring to maintain 'meaty' taste.

4 Use extra water. Some meat products contain polyphospates which hold water, hence inexpensive burgers shrink a lot when cooked.

5 Use some or all re-formed meat.

6 Simplify the packaging.

Note that there are two areas of saving open to industry that do not apply to cost cutting at home.

● Use of recovered meat – Food manufacturers cannot afford to waste even the tiny fragments that are left on the carcass of an animal. So they use machines that compress the carcass and force any meat that remains through a perforated metal drum. This meat is collected and added to food products to reduce the amount of expensive meat that is used.

● Change packaging – the manufacturer can change the type and style of packaging so that it costs less. This may result in the product looking quite different on the supermarket shelf.

Prototype production

Planning is crucial in the production of a prototype food product.

You will need to draw up a production schedule that describes the best order and sequence for production (see page 108). If more than one product is being made at one time, you will need to take this into account and plan for processes to be developed in parallel. You can use flow charts and Gantt charts to help with this (see page 91).

The following Chooser Charts describe some of the methods that you can use to produce prototype food products. Use the information in this section to choose the methods for your design. Get detailed advice and guidance from your teacher on the safest ways to carry out the methods.

Preparation of Food Materials Chooser Chart

Method	Equipment	Applications	Quality control
measuring by weight	kitchen scales	To achieve exact amounts and required ratios in recipes where this is critical.	Observation of readout scale plus careful addition to the scale pan, especially near the end point.
measuring by volume	measuring jug	To achieve exact amounts and required ratios in recipes where this is critical.	Observation of level against scale plus careful addition, especially near the end point.
grating	hand grater food processor	To produce ingredients in the form of shavings and coarse powders.	Selection of grater coarseness plus even pressure on grater. Selection of blade size in processor and length of processing.
sieving	sieve	To remove lumps in powders and ensure even distribution of powdered ingredients.	Selection of sieve coarseness.
cutting to size	knives food processor	To achieve quicker cooking times same cooking times ease of portion control	Observation to ensure consistent use of knife. Consistent rate of addition through cutting plate of food processor. Careful timing if body of processor used, or a slurry may be produced.
cutting out	knives cutters	To control shape of thin-sheet materials such as pastry or biscuit.	Observation to ensure consistent use of knife in free cutting. Spacing cut shapes closely together to avoid waste.
piping	piping bag	To control cross-section of materials that can be extruded.	Even pressure on bag plus observation to ensure consistent movement of nozzle.
rolling out	rolling pin	To control thickness of thin-sheet materials.	Even pressure on roller plus spacers as a depth gauge to ensure thickness required.

Combining Food Materials Chooser Chart

Method	Equipment	Applications	Quality control
rubbing in – usually fat to flour	bare hands, between finger-tips and thumb food processor	Production of pastry / cake mixes.	Observation to ensure nature of end product – the mixture should be: dry have evenly sized, small granules have no large lumps not be dark yellow if a yellow fat has been used. Note it is very easy to over rub-in using a food processor.
creaming – usually fat into dry ingredients	wooden spoon hand-held electric mixer food processor food mixer	Production of pastry/cake mixes.	Observation to ensure nature of end product – the mixture should have a creamy texture throughout.
blending – mixing one or more ingredients together, including a liquid	spoon blender food processor	Production of sauces, mousses.	Observation to ensure nature of end product – a smooth, even texture with no lumps.
whisking to incorporate a high proportion of air	electric mixer food processor hand whisk	Production of sponge mixtures and meringues.	Observation to ensure nature of end product – the foam should: have increased volume be stable. Important to avoid over-beating so timing of beating is important.
kneading – usually bread dough to strengthen the gluten	bare hands, using the fists dough hook in food mixer	Production of breads.	Observation to ensure nature of end product – the dough should be elastic. Elasticity achieved by kneading for a set time.

Cooking Methods Chooser Chart

Cooking method	Equipment	Applications	Quality control
Steaming – the hot steam cooks the food by conduction and latent heat given out when steam condenses to liquid water. Will not brown.	steamer	Puddings and vegetables. Helps vegetables keep flavour and vitamin C.	Temperature maintained at 100°C by production of steam with boiling water. Exact timing is not crucial. Observation of appearance: vegetables should remain crisp, sponge should be well risen and surface spring back when finger-tested.
Boiling – the hot water cooks the food by conduction. Will not brown.	saucepan	Puddings, vegetables and pasta.	Temperature maintained at 100°C by boiling water. Exact timing is not crucial. Observation of appearance: vegetables should remain crisp, pudding should be well risen and surface spring back when finger tested, pasta should be al denté.
Frying – shallow/dry fry. The hot fat cooks the food by conduction.	frying pan wok hot-plate	Thinly sliced foods. A wok for stir-frying, a hot-plate or pan for bacon, sausages and foods that form shallow pools like eggs and chapatis.	Temperature controlled by operator regulating the burner/heater; maximum temperature around 200°C. Exact timing is not crucial. Observation of appearance: vegetables should soften and then brown, meat and fish brown, pierce meat and check juices run clear.
Frying – deep-fat frying. The hot fat cooks the food by conduction, reaching temperatures of 200°C.	deep-fat fryer	Quick-cooking fish, meat, fruit and vegetables in batter, chips and doughnuts.	Temperature controlled by operator regulating the burner/heater; maximum temperature around 200°C. Timing is important as this is a quick-cooking method. Observation of surface colour is also an indication of the extent of cooking.

Cooking Methods Chooser Chart

Cooking method	Equipment	Applications	Quality control
Grilling – the food is cooked by infra-red radiation.	grill toaster	Thinly sliced foods such as sausages, bacon, bread and some vegetables – peppers, mushrooms and tomatoes.	For the grill – temperature controlled by operator regulating the burner/heater. Timing is important as this is a quick-cooking method. For the toaster – automatic timer set by operator. Observation of surface colour is also an indication of the extent of cooking.
Baking – the hot air cooks the food by convection.	oven	Roasting joints of meat and poultry, baking mixtures that rise and set like breads and cakes, and cooking casseroles.	Temperature of oven set by operator using a regulator. Exact timing not crucial for roasting or casseroling. Timing is important for baking, plus observation of colour and springiness of surface.
Pressure cooking – high temperature steam cooks food by conduction and latent heat.	pressure cooker	Casseroles and sponge puddings.	Temperature set by operator using a regulator – maximum temperature 140°C. Timing very important as it is easy to over-cook and food cannot be seen.
Microwaves – the food is cooked by microwave radiation. Will not brown unless heating element also present.	microwave cooker	An alternative to boiling, steaming and baking but not roasting. Defrosting frozen foods, heating ready-cooked convenience foods.	Timing very important as easy to over-cook. Time can be set to the nearest second using control panel.

Finishing Methods Chooser Chart

Method	Equipment		Applications	Quality control
adding a garnish		a range of sizing and shaping tools: scissors, knives, graters	Edible decorations such as a sprig of herbs, chopped herbs, chopped roasted nuts, grated parmesan cheese.	Observation to ensure freshness and appropriate size/shape.
Controlling surface colour				
glazing		saucepan and stirring spoon	To give a shiny appearance to boiled root vegetables, e.g. butter on carrots.	Observation to avoid over-cooking and even coating.
grilling		grill	To give a browned appearance to the surface of foods, e.g. cheese toppings, creme custards.	For the grill – temperature controlled by operator regulating the burner/heater. Timing is important as it is easy to burn the surface.
roasting and baking		oven	To give a browned appearance to the surface of foods, e.g. meats, cakes and biscuits.	Temperature of oven set by operator using a regulator. Exact timing not crucial for meats but essential for cakes and biscuits.
coating and dipping		saucepan and stirring spoon	To cover solid foods with liquid coating, e.g. pasta shells tossed in tomato sauce.	Observation to ensure even, complete covering.
Controlling surface texture				
smoothing		palette knife	To make a surface smooth, e.g. putting icing onto a sponge cake.	Observation to ensure even, complete coverage.
marking		fork	To make a surface textured, e.g. fluffing up top of a shepherd's pie.	Observation to ensure complete coverage.
Controlling shape				
folding		bare hands	To create pastry parcels, e.g. samosa.	Careful handling plus observation to ensure regular, accurate arrangement.
cutting out		knives cutters	To create ribbon and shaped decorations on pies, tarts and pastries.	Observation to ensure consistent use of knife and cutter.
sculpting		knives	To create interesting edible decoration, e.g. radish rosettes.	Observation to ensure consistent use of knife and nature of finished product.
extruding		piping bag	To control cross-section of materials that can be extruded, e.g. icing on a party cake.	Even pressure on bag plus observation to ensure consistent movement of nozzle.
Controlling form				
forming		bare hands baking trays moulds	To create 3D shapes as in marzipan figures, fairy cakes and jellies.	Observation to ensure appropriate shaping. Careful release from trays and moulds.

Catering

The scale of production is an important consideration in the design and manufacture of food products. The last section described the methods used to produce a single prototype product. In this section, the methods used in catering organizations will be described. You should note that while the processes are similar, the scale of production results in significant differences.

Prêt á Manger

'Prêt á manger' is the French phrase for 'ready to eat', and is a chain of London-based food outlets geared towards providing high quality fast food. Its mission is:

> 'to sell the freshest hand-made food of the highest possible quality. We carefully avoid preservatives, additives and obscure chemicals found in much of the 'prepared' and 'fast' food on the market today.'

Prêt á Manger produces a leaflet for consumers explaining what it sells and why it sells it. The following are the features it chooses to highlight:

- the 'mission' statement is about Prêt á Manger's culture, food and its resolution to satisfy customers – it considers itself a business with integrity;
- good quality, service and value for money are the key features;
- new products are introduced every month;
- Prêt á Manger isn't just about the food – it uses recycled paper and biodegradable plastic bags, and tries to use as little packaging as possible;

- It is part of a "Helping the Homeless" project and has a truck on the road to deliver free, fresh food to hostels for the homeless;
- in 1994 it was awarded the 'Sandwich Shop of the Year' award from the British Sandwich Association, and is recommended in several restaurant guides;
- most of its shops are managed by young people who joined the company as sandwich-makers.

Products for a particular group of customers

Prêt á Manger's customers are mainly business people, office workers and tourists. It targets people who think about what they eat and don't mind spending a little extra money on themselves. They may visit Prêt á Manger for a treat as much as for a working lunch or snack. The main features of the menu are shown below.

Each outlet serves a wide range of products

This shop may prepare and serve 1000 sandwiches a day

Method and scale of production

At some sandwich shops, the sandwiches are made up as each customer places an order. In these places there is nearly always a queue and customers have to wait while their sandwiches are prepared. This is not the case at Prêt á Manger. Food is prepared in advance from a set menu. It is classed as 'ready to eat' rather than 'to order'. There is no central production factory, and mass-production techniques are not used. All sandwiches, baguettes, croissants and salads are freshly prepared and packed by hand in the shop in which they are to be sold. Several varieties of cakes are bought-in from a company specializing in traditional methods of making hand-made cakes.

Since 1986, when Prêt á Manger was first set up as a single unit in a kiosk in South London, the company has grown to approximately 30 branches in the London area, serving millions of people. Each shop has its own production levels. Overall 25 000 sandwiches and 13 000 cups of coffee are served daily. Many of the shops have two or three production times during the day. This means that food can be served and eaten soon after it is prepared – you shouldn't find a sandwich made at 7.30 a.m. in the fridge at 3.00 p.m. You should find one that was perhaps prepared at 12.00 or 1.00 p.m.!

A 'day dot' system of stock control is used, which means that there is a 'first in – first out' system on all incoming deliveries. Much of the food to be used is fresh, so it is kept under controlled refrigeration.

Production levels are calculated according to previous sales and past experience of the staff. When a new shop is set up, it is a case of trial and error, and the production level is set on the high side initially and adjusted as necessary. Main ingredients are weighed out the day before, when the number of sandwiches to be produced for the next day is set. Certain days of the week may be busier than others and the production manager will take this into account when making decisions. Frozen products which need to defrost are put into refrigerators overnight.

A systems approach to batch production

Food is produced in batches throughout the day. The number of batches will depend on production levels and how long the shop stays open – some close at 3.30 p.m., some at 11.00 p.m., opening at 8.00 a.m. By preparing the food at varying times there is more control over stock and turnover. For example, if the shop is not busy, the size of the production run can be altered.

Cheeses and meats are sliced in advance. Short-life products such as tomatoes are sliced just before use. Production lines are set up, so French brie and tomato on granary bread might be made like this:

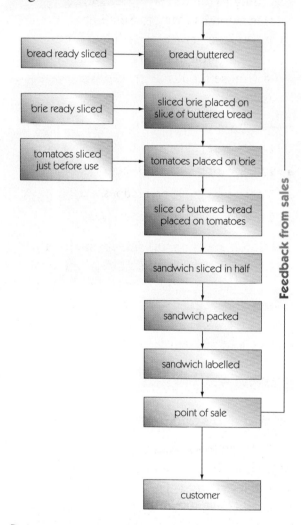

The flow chart turns into the assembly line for the mass production of sandwiches

A large hotel

Who uses the hotel?

The sort of customers using the hotel changes according to the time of year. During the summer months (May to September) the main customers are people on holiday. From September through to April the customers are mainly those on business. The balance would be as follows:

- 49 per cent corporate business;
- 21 per cent conference business;
- 20 per cent holiday and tour bookings;
- 5 per cent special promotions;
- 5 per cent staff rate/special offers.

The emphasis is on value for money for the tourist customers and on a more high quality, attentive service for business clients. The hotel prides itself in preparing delicious food, with plenty of variety and an emphasis on healthy cuisine and seasonal dishes.

How much food is used?

The average amount of food produced on a daily basis is:

- 130 breakfasts
- 100 lunches
- 100 dinners.

This involves the following daily food orders:

- 240 eggs
- 13.5 kg sausages
- 11.25 kg bacon
- 13.5 kg tomatoes
- 12 loaves of bread
- 34 litres of milk
- 18 kg beef or lamb
- 22.5 kg potatoes
- 31.5 kg fresh vegetables

Some ingredients are ordered according to a formula. For example, it is estimated that each guest usually consumes the following each day:

- 200 g meat
- 250 g potatoes
- 125 ml milk.

The Head Chef uses his or her experience to order other ingredients. This is based on how popular certain menu items are and what the daily consumption of food is likely to be given the numbers staying in the hotel and any special events.

The hotel has a list of regular suppliers (butcher, baker, greengrocer, etc.) provided by Head Office. They are made aware of the strict standards expected by the hotel. If a supplier fails to meet these standards the delivery is returned and a replacement supplier is found.

The Head Chef is responsible for ordering all foodstuffs and checking deliveries to ensure that the correct products have been delivered and that they are of an acceptable standard. Food is then stored safely and hygienically. Stock control is important to make sure that there are enough ingredients, but minimal wastage.

The ordering and receipt of foods is managed and controlled using a computer. Each Saturday a stock report is printed off the computer in the accounts department, and the stock-take is completed in the evening by the Head Chef. In this process the chef records which food materials are in stock, how much of each and whether anything has run out completely. The stock sheet is passed back to accounts which, on Monday mornings, processes all the data. This analysis takes into account all deliveries, items already in stock, the consumption of those items and the total revenue for all food sold during the previous week, and produces a balance sheet for the kitchen within the hotel. This shows whether the kitchen is making a profit or a loss.

Handling food in large quantities

Food is handled in large quantities. For example, potatoes are delivered in sacks. When required, they are washed in large industrial-sized machines called 'rumblers' which propel the vegetables around with water and rub them against a hard, scaly wall inside the machine which removes the skin. They are then either cooked in a conventional oven or steamed. If the food is to be used later, it is placed in a blast-chiller. This device quickly brings the item down to a safe temperature so that it can be refrigerated until needed. When an order is received the vegetables are taken from the refrigerator and placed in a steamer to bring them up to serving temperature.

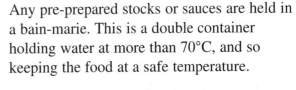
This evening meal requires a complex production schedule

Any pre-prepared stocks or sauces are held in a bain-marie. This is a double container holding water at more than 70°C, and so keeping the food at a safe temperature.

Meat is dealt with differently, as the more meat there is, the more time and oven space is needed to cook it. So small joints of meat (7–9 kg) are prepared and cooked in advance. They are then held in a hot-cupboard until required. The table below summarizes the production schedule for an evening meal.

All á la carte dishes are freshly prepared. Other dishes are cooked in advance to speed up the service time. They are then either steamed to reheat them, or reheated in an oven.

All kitchen staff are trained to minimize waste when preparing and cooking foods. They also use ingredients twice wherever it is safe to do so. For example, carrot peel or broccoli stems can be used for stocks or soups. Chicken wings can be marinated and served as cold hors d'oeuvres (a starter dish to a meal).

	Dishes	Preparation	Storage	Serving
First course	chicken liver paté	cooked, chilled	in a refrigerator	sliced and placed on plate with salad
	melba toast	toasted	in a dry-tin	arranged in a basket
	side salad	washed, cut to required sizes/pieces	in cold-store	arranged on plate
Main course	rump steak	none	in cold-store	grilled to order
	provençale sauce	pre-prepared	in cold-store	served from bain-marie
	new potatoes	steamed and chilled	in cold-store	reheated to order
	carrots	steamed and chilled	in cold-store	reheated to order
	beans	steamed and chilled	in cold-store	reheated to order
Dessert	chocolate gateaux	cooked and decorated	in cold-store	decorate plate with fresh strawberries
				arrange slice on plate
				dust plate with icing sugar

Industrial production

Achieving quality by control

When a food is produced, control systems are used to achieve quality. When you make a food product, *you* are the control system. You:

- weigh out and mix the ingredients;
- set the oven temperature;
- carry out procedures according to set times to achieve particular results;
- use your skills of observation to note when the colour, texture or flavour is right.

In large-scale food production in industry, all this is achieved using computer systems.

The role of sensors

A key feature of control systems is the electronic sensors used to detect the changes that take place as food is processed. Here are some examples.

- Photo-cells – these are light sensitive and are used to detect the presence or absence of objects. If the light beam can reach the photo-cell there is nothing in the way. If it can't reach the photo-cell, there is. So, for example, photo-cells can be used to check the level of contents in clear containers.

- Load-cells – these give an electrical signal according to how much they are loaded, so they are used to monitor weight. For example, as a tank fills it puts a load on the cell which provides a signal to the control system about how empty or full the tank is.

- Metal detectors – these use changes in a magnetic field to detect the presence of metals in food.

◑ *Technology requires responsible people*

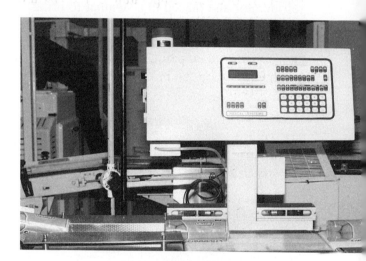

◑ *A load cell checking weight of biscuits*

- Thermistors and thermocouples – these are used for monitoring temperature. So, for example, they would be used to control the temperature of ovens.

- Reflectometers – these measure the intensity and colour of light reflected from objects, so they are used to monitor the change in colour of food products as they are baked.

The importance of central processing

Information from the sensors is passed back to a central processing unit (CPU) which can display the information in a variety of forms:

- numbers on a digital readout;
- a needle moving across a dial;
- changes in a graph that is being continuously printed;
- lights coming on or buzzers sounding.

The CPU can also control the response of the food production system to this information. So in the case of jam production (see page 196–198), once the temperature of the mixture has reached a certain level the CPU instructs the heaters to turn off and a valve to open so that the jam can be pumped to the jar-filling machinery. Using the information from sensors in this way is called feedback (see *Strategies* page 89 and the Case Study on page 46).

Moving raw materials

Liquid foods can be stored in vats, tanks or silos. They are moved by being pumped through pipes from the storage container into the vessels where they will be processed. Valves control the route of the liquid through the pipes. The amount of liquid moved can be monitored using flow meters. Both the pipes and the storage vessels are temperature controlled to prevent the action of microbes and to ensure a consistency suitable for pumping.

Solid ingredients in the form of powders and pellets are stored in silos. They are drawn off from the bottom of the silo and mixed with a flow of air so that they can be pumped along pipes. They are transported to hoppers where the solid settles out as the air passes through a filter.

Analogue display of pressure and digital display of temperature

Control panels for moving materials

Complex pipe work, pumps and valves are required

Food production

Mixing ingredients

Most food products involve mixing and combining more than one ingredient. Examples include mixing and kneading biscuit, pastry or bread doughs. The type of mixers used are rather like large-scale versions of a domestic mixer, designed to deal with the much larger quantities of ingredients that are being mixed. This can be achieved by using more powerful motors and by the design and action of the mixing blades or paddles. Rotating drums may also be used to help move the ingredients being mixed. Mixtures can also be passed through rollers if it is necessary to break up clumps. Alternatively, 'impactors', where one stream of powder is blown into another at high speed, may be used.

Successful mixing depends on:

- weighing quantities accurately;
- condition of raw ingredients;
- using the appropriate type of mixer;
- precise control of mixer speed and length of process time.

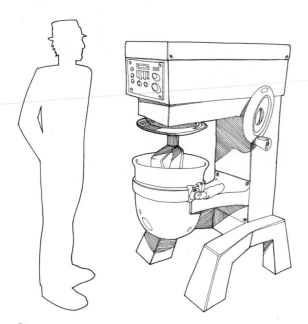

This planetary mixer can hold up to 80 litres

A multideck oven for large batches

Heating food

In the food industry a variety of ovens are used. Here are some examples.

- *Travelling ovens* (which may be several metres wide and several hundred metres long) enable the passage of high levels of 'traffic' by means of a conveyor belt which passes through heated oven chambers. Each zone of the oven has an access point for quality checking to be carried out.

- *Multi-deck ovens* are used mainly for small, in-store cake baking. They have several chambers each with heating elements (burners or pipes), and the top and bottom heaters can be controlled individually in each of them.

- *Reel ovens* have baking trays which revolve around a central axis to ensure even baking.

- *Rotary-rack* ovens are large enough for racks of baking trays to be wheeled into them, attached to the roof and rotated for even baking. Hot air passes over the items being baked by forced convection through vents in the chamber walls.

Cooling food

Cooling and freezing food is an important aspect of food production. Processes such as cook-chill and cook-freeze as well as long-term storage require rapid cooling. The key to the industrial process is using fans to circulate air over refrigerated elements and then over the food. This process is known as **blast-chilling** or **blast-freezing**. The movement of the air reduces the insulating properties of air on the surface of the food and enables the food to be cooled very rapidly. Information from temperature sensors is fed back to the CPU which stops the cooling process when the desired temperature is reached and holds it at that level.

The importance of HACCP

HACCP stands for Hazard Analysis of Critical Control Points, and is being used in the food industry as a means of quality assurance. It involves the manufacturer analysing and identifying any possible hazards (in terms of food hygiene and safety) that may occur during production. A 'critical control point' is a point where control can be applied to prevent or reduce a hazard. This process is useful for upgrading the performance of existing systems as it identifies clearly where improvements could be made. The existing control systems can be adapted or redesigned to meet the requirements indicated by HACCP. New manufacturing systems can be designed with HACCP built into the specification.

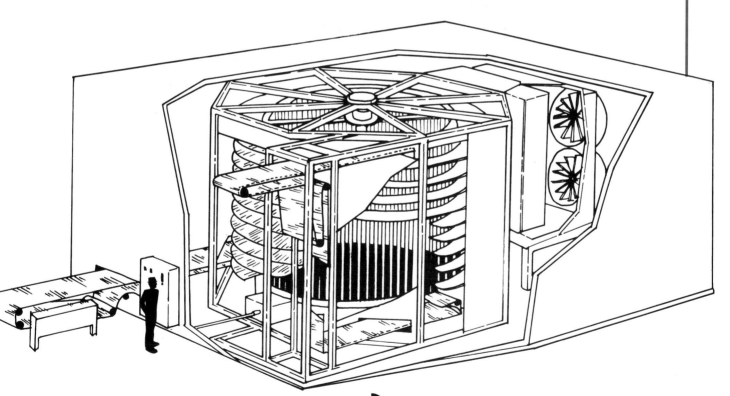

◗ *A large air blast freezer*

Manufacturing jam

Getting the mixture right

Jam is really only a mixture of fruit, sugar, water and a gelling agent (pectin) which has been boiled, but getting even this simple mixture right presents a challenge to the food industry. The overall process is shown below.

◗ *The finished product*

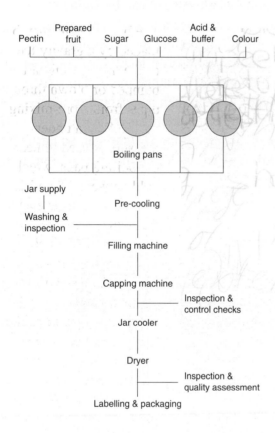

◗ *Jam manufacture by the traditional pan method*

For a food product to be called a jam it has to contain a minimum amount of sugar and fruit. So getting the ingredients in these right proportions for the jam is the first problem. Two-thirds of jam is sugar which comes from the sugar in the fruit plus added sucrose and glucose syrup. It is important to control the extra acid which has to be added and this is achieved by using citric acid and sodium citrate, a buffer which prevents the acid level (the pH of the mixture) from changing. The low pH is required to activate the pectin which causes the jam to set. Measuring the pH of the gel in the boiler is difficult so samples are drawn off and diluted with 50% water to give a solution which can be measured accurately.

Boiling the mixture

The boiling process is important for several reasons:

- it concentrates the mixture by removing excess water;
- it causes the sucrose to form other sugars (this is called inversion);
- it develops the flavour;
- it changes the texture of the fruit;
- it destroys yeasts and moulds (in the open pan process).

If the boiling is carried out at atmospheric pressure, the product reaches a temperature of approximately 105° C. The two major manufacturers in the UK use a vacuum boiling process in which the boiling water is carried out under reduced pressure. The bulk of excess water is removed at 60–70° C. There are advantages to this method. Less heat energy is required to boil the jam and at this lower temperature there is less caramelization which reduces unwanted flavours and undesirable colour changes.

Jam-making under reduced pressure

The boiling pans may be loaded by a gravity feed, or the mixture might be pumped or blown through pipes from a pre-mixing vessel. Steam under pressure is used to heat the boiling pans, which hold between 75 and 100 kg of jam mixture each in the reduced pressure process and as much as 1000 kg in the open pan process. The steam is circulated in a jacket surrounding the pan, and may also be supplied to internal coils for faster heating. Pans may be used in sets of between four and eight so that a continuous supply of jam can be obtained. In the past the jam was poured out by tipping the pan, but most factories now use a bottom outlet valve.

In the open pan process each pan has a hood above it which is connected to an extractor system so the water vapour is removed as it evaporates from the jam. Once loaded the steam supply is switched on and the mix is boiled until it reaches the right sugar content. This is usually checked with a refractometer. This measures the amount that the mixture bends a ray of light. Refractometers used in jam making are calibrated in sugar content.

Filling the jars

Filling is usually carried out automatically by a machine which uses a piston to deliver exact amounts into each jar. The jars are cleaned before use. In modern factories this is carried out with compressed air which flushes out any foreign bodies particularly very tiny pieces of glass which water may cause to stick to the side of the jar. The jars are preheated before filling and travel into the filling machine on a carousel The largest filling machines can fill 400 jars per minute. Capping is carried out immediately after filling using a steam flow machine that ensures air is removed from the jar and softens the lining in the lid to ensure a good seal.

Finishing off

The hot jars of jam, not less than 85°C, are then cooled by spraying with water. The first spray of water is at 60°C to avoid thermal shock, which could crack the jars, and also to ensure a slow initial cooling so that 'after boiling' under reduced pressure does not take place. The later water sprays are at 20°C. The wet jars are dried by an air blower and tested to ensure that each one is hermetically sealed. This is done by a machine which checks that the lids are slightly concave (pushed inwards). This is due to the effect of atmospheric pressure on the lid when there is a vacuum inside the jar. That is why you hear a 'pop' when you open a jar of jam for the first time; it is the sound of air rushing in to fill the vacuum. Any jars that do not have a slightly concave lid are rejected automatically.

◑ *Ready for despatch*

The jars then pass on to a visual inspection area where lighting conditions allow inspectors to spot any undesirable characteristics such as bubble formation, fruit flotation, foreign material, etc. The jars then pass to labelling machines and are finally packed in either cases or trays with shrink-wrap film.

Frozen vegetables

Most vegetables freeze, store and thaw well. As a result, frozen vegetables occupy an important place in the frozen food industry. Most vegetables contain enzymes which cause loss of colour and unacceptable flavours during freezing. To prevent this the enzymes are inactivated before freezing, usually by means of a steam or water blanche. Mechanical damage during harvesting accelerates flavour loss, tainting and discoloration, so it is important to minimize the time between harvesting and blanching. Before being blanched the vegetables are treated so that they are completely edible. This may involve washing, sorting, grading, trimming, peeling, shucking, etc. Manufacturers try to achieve a 'picked to frozen' time of less than two hours!

Most vegetables benefit from quick freezing because it causes less damage to cells and results in a crisper texture in the finished product. Blast-freezing is usually used. The nutritional value of vegetables is generally not impaired by freezing. Vitamin C content is reduced, but if storage temperatures are maintained at -18°C or colder, 80 per cent of this vitamin will still be present after a year.

The most popular frozen vegetables are potato chips or French fries. The potatoes are harvested in the autumn and stored in warehouses. If the weather is cold they have to be left for a 'conditioning' period to reduce the sugar content, which can give rise to dark-coloured chips. Colour control of the finished product is also achieved by washing surface sugars out of the raw chips in a warm-water blanche and then deliberately adding back a low level of sugar in order to achieve the desired light golden yellow colour after frying.

The quality of the starting potato is important. A high-solid potato (18–24 per cent) will produce an opaque, firm and even floury texture chip, while a low-solid (12–16 per cent) gives a soggy, translucent chip which is unacceptable to many consumers.

Food production

20% — red meats, turkey mince

30% — cheeses, cooked meats, cured and processed meats, cooked food in general, chicken pieces, duck, turkey

50% — chicken– whole, pizzas, pastries, pies, pasta, oily fish, bakery products, breaded meats, fish, poultry

5% 5% 90% — prepared salads, prepared vegetables, prepared fruits

30% 30% 40% — white fish, crustaceans, shellfish

100% — greated cheese, coffee, nuts, cereals, dried herbs and spices, dairy products

100% — bread, biscuits, rolls

Key
- Carbon dioxide
- Oxygen
- Nitrogen

Gas mixtures for modified atmosphere packaging

Modified atmosphere packaging

'Airs' that are different

Food manufacturers are always looking for ways to extend the shelf-life of products. A major advance in this area has been the introduction of modified atmosphere packaging. The goods in this sort of packaging are not surrounded by ordinary air but by a mixture of gases specially formulated to prevent the food from deteriorating, hence the term 'modified atmosphere'. Different foods require different mixtures of gases, as shown in the diagram opposite. Of course the added protection only lasts until the package is opened – once ordinary air is let in, the food product will start to deteriorate normally.

The effects of different gases

The oxygen in the air causes oxidation resulting in fats becoming rancid and salads turning brown. Generally, oxygen is excluded from modified atmosphere packaging, but it is present in some cases. For example:

- it helps red meat retain its colour;
- it maintains respiration in fruit and vegetables;
- it prevents bacteria and fungi growing on fish and vegetables.

Nitrogen is an inert gas and is used to exclude oxygen. It is also used as a 'balance gas' to make up the difference in the gas mixture and to prevent the package from collapsing where the products inside absorb carbon dioxide (like bread) and consume oxygen (red meats).

Carbon dioxide delays the growth of bacteria, and the higher the level of this gas the longer the shelf-life. However, because carbon dioxide is soluble in both fats and water, most foods absorb this gas. High levels of carbon dioxide will cause tainting, drip loss and package collapse. A compromise therefore has to be reached between extending the shelf-life and incurring these negative effects. When carbon dioxide is required to control bacterial growth, a minimum of 20 per cent should be used. However for prepared vegetables, fruits and salads, high levels of carbon dioxide cause damage and the level of the gas should be kept below 15 per cent.

Food poisoning

Food poisoning results from eating or drinking something that has been contaminated. The symptoms are unpleasant:

- abdominal pain (stomach ache);
- diarrhoea ('the runs');
- vomiting (being sick);
- nausea (feeling sick);
- fever (unusually high temperature).

These symptoms can occur between two hours and three days after eating or drinking contaminated food and can persist for up to a week. In exceptional cases, if untreated, they can lead to death.

The incidence of food poisoning appears to be on the increase, as shown by the graph below.

▶ *Food poisoning is no fun!*

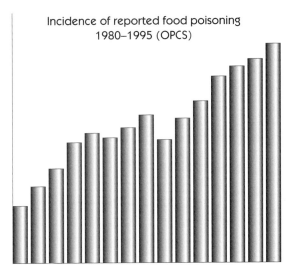

Incidence of reported food poisoning 1980–1995 (OPCS)

▶ *Can you identify the trend, if any, in the number of reported cases of food poisoning over the past 15 years?*

Causes of food poisoning

There are three main sources of contamination.

- *Chemical contamination* – substances such as pesticides and fertilizers can enter the food chain and cause illness.

- *Bacterial contamination* – some bacteria that grow on food are harmful to us, although they may not affect the taste of the food. Other bacteria cause food to rot and are known as **food spoilage bacteria**. The bacteria themselves do not harm us, but eating the spoiled food may make us ill.

- *Food-borne diseases* – some diseases are carried by food and water. These include typhoid, cholera and dysentery. This is sometimes called cross contamination.

Bacterial contamination

Sources of bacterial contamination

It is bacterial contamination that causes most food poisoning. There are many sources of bacterial contamination as shown below:

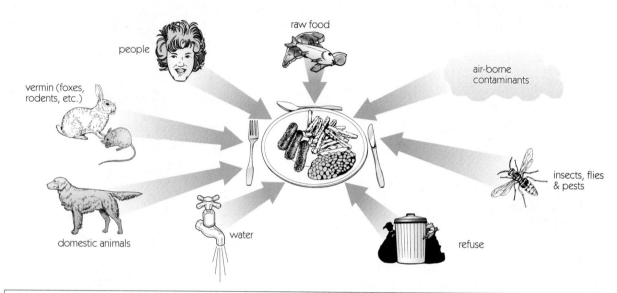

Type of food poisoning	Source of bacteria	Onset period	Symptoms & duration	Incidence	Main cause
THE MAIN CAUSES OF FOOD POISONING					
Salmonella	raw meat, milk, eggs, poultry, carriers (pets, rodents, terrapins), sewage & water	6–72 hours (usually 12 –36 hours)	abdominal pain, diarrhoea, vomiting & fever (1–7 days)	high	eggs, poultry
Clostridium Perfringens (toxin in the intestine)	animal & human excreta, soil, dust, insects & raw meat	8–22 hours (usually 12 –18 hours)	abdominal pain & diarrhoea vomiting is rare (12–48 hours)	medium	ingestion of soil
Staphylococcus aureus	human nose, mouth, skin, boils & cuts, raw milk from cows or goats with mastitis	1–6 hours	abdominal pain, vomiting, prostration & subnormal temperatures (6–24 hours)	low	from ear, nose & throat infections, coughs & sneezes
Campylobacter jejuni	raw meat, raw milk, untreated water	2–10 days	diarrhoea	high	poorly cooked meat
RARER CAUSES OF FOOD POISONING					
E. coli 0157	undercooked meat, untreated milk	3–8 days	bloody diarrhoea, acute kidney failure	very low	poorly cooked meat
Listeria monocytogenes	raw chicken, untreated milk	a few days – 3 weeks	influenza-like symptoms with persistent fever	very low	poorly cooked chicken
Clostridium botulinum	soil and animal intestines	18–36 weeks	tiredness, weakness, vertigo, double vision, diificulty in speaking	very rare	ingestion of contaminated soil or offal

Bacterial multiplication

Bacteria can multiply quickly if the conditions for growth are right. As the diagram below shows, if there is food, warmth and moisture then a single bacterium may become over a half a million bacteria in about three hours.

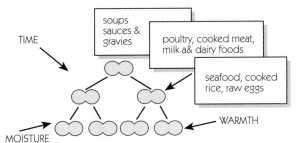

Time (minutes)	No. of bacteria
0	∞
10	∞∞
20	∞∞∞∞
30	∞∞∞∞∞∞∞∞
40	∞∞∞∞∞∞∞∞∞∞∞∞∞∞∞∞
50	∞∞∞∞∞∞∞∞∞∞∞∞∞∞∞∞∞∞∞∞∞∞∞∞∞∞∞∞∞∞∞∞
60	64
70	128
80	256
90	512
100	1024
110	2048
120	4096
130	8192
140	16384
150	32768
160	65536
170	129536
180	259072
190	518144

Bacterial growth under the right conditions is very rapid – one bacterium can divide every 10 minutes

Preventing bacterial contamination

You can break into this chain of bacterial growth by following these simple rules whenever you are going to handle food.

1 Personal hygiene

- Always wash your hands:

    before entering the food-preparation area;

    before touching food;

    after handling raw meat/poultry;

    after using the toilet;

    after coughing/sneezing;

    after blowing your nose;

    after touching your face/hair;

    after using chemicals or cleaning agents.

- Always keep your hair clean and covered.

- Keep all open wounds, cuts, grazes and boils covered with waterproof dressing.

- Never wear jewellery in a food-preparation area.
- Do not enter the area if you have diarrhoea or vomiting.
- Always wear clean overalls and change aprons frequently – protective clothing should not be worn outside the food area.

2 Proper food preparation procedures

The key to this is preventing cross-contamination between raw foods that are likely to have some bacterial contamination (meat and poultry) and cooked foods in which the bacteria have been killed by cooking. Here are some guidelines:

- identify separate and distinct areas of the workplace for raw meat/poultry and for cooked food;

- clean work surfaces thoroughly after each operation;

- wash kitchen equipment and utensils thoroughly after each operation;

- keep utensils used for preparation of raw meat/poultry separate from those used for other foods;

- if possible, colour code equipment to help identify their use, for example RED for raw meat and poultry, BLUE for fish, BROWN for cooked meats, GREEN for vegetables and fruit, WHITE for general use and bakery;

- the kitchen environment should be clean – dirt, rubbish and waste food not only carry bacteria but they also encourage pests – keep waste bins covered and away from fresh food and supplies;

- establish and follow a regular cleaning schedule each day for floors, walls, windows, work surfaces, ovens, grills and heavy/large items of equipment.

3 Proper storage and cooking procedures

The key here is to keep the food at temperatures outside the danger zone of 4°C to 63°C. It is important to keep hot food hot and cold food cold. The reasons for this are shown in the panel.

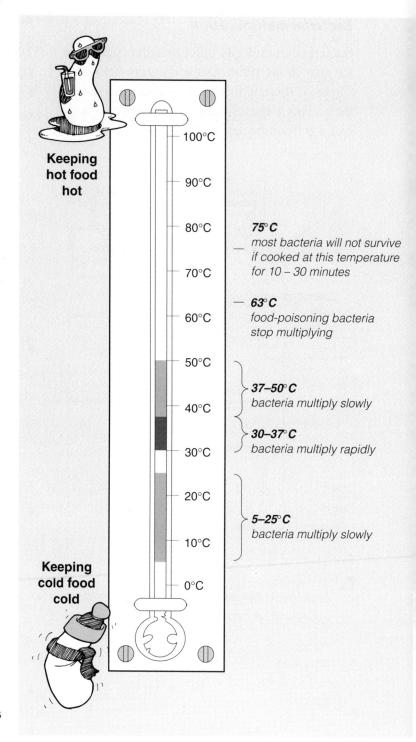

Keeping hot food hot

75°C
most bacteria will not survive if cooked at this temperature for 10 – 30 minutes

63°C
food-poisoning bacteria stop multiplying

37–50°C
bacteria multiply slowly

30–37°C
bacteria multiply rapidly

5–25°C
bacteria multiply slowly

Keeping cold food cold

Food hygiene and the law

There are various Acts of Parliament and regulations that have been designed to protect the public from food that is unfit to eat. The **Food Hygiene (General) Regulations, 1970** are concerned directly with protecting the public from outbreaks of food poisoning. They set out the rules of food hygiene applicable to every establishment that processes or sells food to the public. The regulations are enforced by Local Authority Environmental Health Officers, and failure to comply with the regulations can result in prosecution – both of companies and of individuals. The penalties range from fines through to imprisonment. The main parts of the regulations are summarized below.

Premises where food is prepared and/or sold have to reach minimum standards of design and layout, construction and hygiene. Rooms must be kept clean, properly equipped, properly organized, well lit and ventilated, free from waste and refuse, have toilets separate from the food areas, and have storage for employees' personal belongings.

Food premises must have a clean supply of water with facilities for washing food, utensils and equipment. Kitchen sinks and hand-basins must have hot and cold running water. Hand-basins must be provided with appropriate hand-drying facilities as well as soap and a nail-brush. Washrooms and toilets must be clean, well maintained, well lit and well ventilated. They must also have 'wash your hands' notices prominently displayed.

The law also requires all equipment to be kept clean and in good working order and makes all employees who handle food responsible for guarding against food becoming contaminated.

The **Food Hygiene (Amendment) Regulations, 1990 and 1991** require the following to be stored at or below 5°C:

- soft cheeses;
- patés;
- cooked food (containing meat, fish, eggs, cheese, cereals, pulses or vegetables) usually eaten without cooking/reheating;
- smoked or cured fish;
- cut or sliced smoked and cured meats;
- sandwiches made from meat, fish, eggs or soft cheese (unless for sale within 4 hours of making).

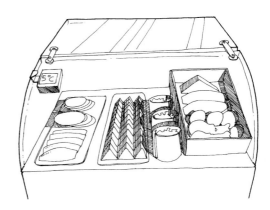

Note that in September 1995 additional temperature legislation was introduced. This requires chilled food to be held at a maximum of 8°C unless on display for sale within 2 hours. Kept-hot food has to be at a minimum of 63°C unless on display for sale within 2 hours.

Food safety and the law

The Food Hygiene Regulations are mainly concerned with where and how food is prepared. The **Food Safety Act, 1990** regulates the sale of food for human consumption. This Act is important to everyone who works in the production, processing, storage, distribution and sale of food products – no matter how large or small the organization. It also applies to all stages of the food production chain, including crops and animals, as well as items that come into contact with the food once it has been produced (like packaging, wrapping and cooking dishes). It also applies to completely synthetic products such as slimming aids and vitamin supplements, as well as the water used in making food products.

The strict regulations of the Food Safety Act have the following requirements for each of the ingredients in a food product:

- it must not have been made dangerous or harmful to health;

- it must not be unfit for human consumption due to contamination;

- it must not contain anything that would make it unreasonable to expect someone to eat it;

- it must not be injurious to health.

The Food Safety Act gives local authorities certain powers to enter food premises to check, inspect, test and approve equipment, ingredients, products, etc. The local authorities employ two sorts of officers to do this.

- Trading Standards Officers deal with the labelling of food, what goes into it and cases of chemical contamination.

- Environmental Health Officers deal with hygiene, micro-biological contamination of food and foods which are unfit for human consumption.

In most cases, the Trading Standards or Environmental Health Officers will issue **Improvement Notices** when they discover something is not quite right, but they have a lot of power to take action if the problem is not put right in a reasonable time. If a business is convicted of a breach of the regulations, the company, shop or factory could have part or all of its operation stopped or closed down by a **Prohibition Order**.

The food industry is using technology to develop new food materials, such as tomatoes, which are genetically engineered for a long shelf-life, and new food processing techniques such as irradiation to prevent spoiling. The Food Safety Act makes provision for inspecting and testing these developments to ensure public safety.

Food labelling

The **1984 Food Labelling Regulations** require pre-packed foods to be labelled. Under the Food Safety Act, 1990 government ministers are given the power to make regulations about what information must be shown on food, and how it must be shown. The information which must be show is detailed below.

(1) Name
The name must describe the food, e.g. 'Chocolate Delight' must also be described as chocolate and cream dessert. Strawberry yoghurt must contain strawberries, but 'strawberry-flavoured' yoghurt need not.

(2) Ingredients
These must be listed in descending order of inclusion by weight. If added water is more than 5% of contents, it must be listed as an ingredient. Additives must be shown by name and E number.

(3) Date mark
Most foods are now date marked. The main exceptions are long-life foods (last more than 18 months). The date marked is the date up to and including which the food will remain at its best if stored correctly. Look for the words 'Best Before' and 'Sell By'.

(4) Storage instructions
The label must give instructions for the best storage methods for the food product.

(5) Name & address
The name and address of the manufacturer, packagers or seller within the EU must be on the label.

(6) Place of origin
If a food has been imported and then packed by a manufacturer in England, it may be misleading if the country of origin is not mentioned on the label.

(7) Preparation
There should be instructions for preparation if necessary (for example, with cake mixes).

(8) Quantity or weight
Most foods are labelled with the weight in grams. An 'e' after the weight means that the manufacturer is complying with the average system of weights and measures which is common throughout the EU.

Special claims
Foods which claim to have special properties, e.g. 'rich in vitamin C', should be labelled with extra information to support this claim.

Nutritional labelling

As well as the information required by law, many people (both consumers and manufacturers) believe that other information is helpful to customers and should be shown on labelling. For example, by law labels do not have to show the amount of fat, sugar or fibre contained in a product but this information is helpful to consumers who wish to eat a healthy diet. The **COMA Report** (Committee on Medical Aspects of Food Policy) recommends that the percentage by weight of fat and the proportion of saturated and polyunsaturated fat in a food product should be shown on the label. Lower fat products are believed to reduce the risk of heart disease.

Similarly, people who follow special diets either for medical reasons (such as food allergies, coeliac sufferers and diabetics) or for personal reasons (such as vegetarians) would benefit from more detailed information about the food products available to them. Many supermarkets provide this detailed nutritional information voluntarily – some even see it as a marketing technique to encourage customers to buy their goods. Many of these companies use either symbols or colour coding to identify products of a particular type, and most produce free leaflets for customers.

Food additives

The 1990 Food Safety Act makes it illegal to add anything to food or food products that may cause damage to our health. Additives are substances added to our food in order to improve its quality in some way. There are roughly 3500 additives currently in use by food manufacturers. Some of these are natural, for example lecithin (E322) which is made from soya beans and is used to stop some foods from separating either during cooking or afterwards, before they are consumed. Others are synthetic like butylated hydroxy anisole, or BHA (E320) which is used to prevent oxidation in things like cheese spread and stock cubes.

E numbers are used to identify some of the additives used by food manufacturers. Of the permitted additives, 280 have been given an E number, which indicates that it has been approved by the countries in the European Union (EU). Since 1986, additives must be listed by type and chemical name or number in the ingredients list on food packaging.

How do additives affect our food?

There are four groups of additives and each one affects either the taste, the texture, the colour or the shelf-life of the food product in which it is used. The panel below gives some examples of these groups.

Taste

Flavourings: These are the most common form of additive and there are over 3000 of them. At present they are not controlled by additive regulations – a label only has to say that 'flavour' or 'flavourings' have been added.

Flavour enhancers: These are not flavours but substances that make existing flavours taste stronger. The best known is E621 – monosodium glutamate which is often used in savoury foods.

Artificial sweeteners: These are often used in foods for slimmers and diabetics as well as other foods. The most common examples are saccharin and aspartame.

Texture

Emulsifiers and stabilizers: Emulsifiers help oil and water to mix together and stabilizers prevent them from separating again. Used in low-fat spreads as well as sweet and savoury foods. A common example is E407.

Thickeners: These act like flour or cornflour in a sauce, e.g. E412 guar gum, which is used in soups and meringue mixes. Another popular thickener is modified starch.

Anti-caking agents: For example, E504 magnesium carbonate. These stop lumps forming in powdery foods, like salt, to keep it free flowing.

Gelling agents: Used to make food set, as in jams, desserts, etc. Pectin (E440) is a common natural gelling agent.

Raising agents: Make food rise, for example E500 (sodium bicarbonate) or baking powder.

The use of additives is controversial and the table below summarizes the arguments used by those for and against additives.

FOR ADDITIVES	AGAINST ADDITIVES
• They improve the taste and appearance of food products.	• Some cause allergic reactions.
• They increase shelf-life.	• Some affect certain medical conditions.
• Some help to prevent food poisoning.	• Many additives are purely for cosmetic reasons, especially colourings, flavour enhancers and flavourings.
• Without them some new food products or manufacturing processes would not be possible.	• They may have long-term effects we don't know about.
• Their use is strictly regulated by law already.	

Colour

There are 58 permitted natural and artificial food colouring additives.

Natural colouring: Good examples are caramel (E150) which is made by over-cooking sugar, and chlorophyll (E140) a green colouring obtained from plants.

Artificial colouring: There are only 20 permitted artificial colours – perhaps the best known is tartrazine (E102) which is yellow.

Shelf-life

Preservatives: These help food keep longer, delaying the spoilage of food by preventing the growth of microbes.

Antioxidants: These stop oils and fats from combining with oxygen and going rancid ('off' or bad). A good example is E320 (butylated hydroxy anisole) which is used in cheese spread, beef stock cubes, biscuits and margarine.

Health and safety
in food product design and manufacture

Important idea

If you are to avoid accidents and harm you need a set of criteria to help you look at situations. These are **hazard**, **risk**, **risk assessment** and **risk control**. A hazard is anything which might cause harm or damage. The chance of a hazard causing harm or damage is called the risk. You can work out how big the risk is by thinking about whether the harm or damage is likely to happen. This is called risk assessment. Risk control is the action taken to ensure that the harm or damage is less likely to happen.

Looking at an unfamiliar situation

In the manufacture of food products there are two main safety issues – the safety of the people working in the factory that makes the product and the safety of the people who eat the product. These are clearly interlinked. Poor hygiene in the factory will affect both workers and consumers.

The following example shows the manufacture of biscuits. The table on the next page describes each stage, with notes showing hazard identification, risk assessment and risk control for those who work in the factory and those who consume the product. You can use this approach to keeping safe and free from harm anywhere – at home, at school or at work.

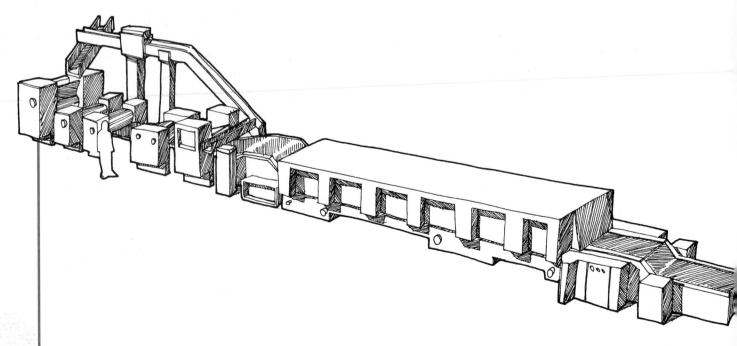

Activity	Hazards	Risk assessment	Risk control
Selecting the ingredients	*Workers* some materials have toxic effects eg baking powder causes nose bleeds; flour is very inflammable	high	ensure materials to be used are vetted for possible effects
	Consumers ingredients need to be suitable for human consumption	high	ensure ingredients are from reputable supplier
Receiving the ingredients	*Workers* possible toxic effects strain injuries	high	staff training, face masks, gloves fork lift trucks
	Consumers contamination	high	sealed containers
Storing the ingredients	*Workers* possible toxic effects strain injuries	high	staff training, face masks, gloves fork lift trucks
	Consumers contamination spoilage pest attack	high	sealed containers appropriate conditions pest control
Preparing and mixing the ingredients	*Workers* possible toxic effects strain injuries	high	staff training, face masks, gloves
	Consumers contamination	high	hygienic practice temperature control
Cooking the product	*Workers* burns	high	enclosed ovens, staff training
	Consumers incomplete cooking	high	temperature control
Packaging the product	*Workers* boredom	high	staff training
	Consumers contamination	high	hygienic practice
Storing the product	*Workers* strain injuries	high	staff training, fork lift trucks
	Consumers pest attack	high	pest control
Dispatching the product	*Workers* strain injuries	high	staff training, fork lift trucks
	Consumers physical damage	medium	adequate packaging, good handling

Note that the risk assesment is almost always high because unless the controls are in place it is likely that harm will result to either consumers or workers.

Manufacturers have a legal responsibility to make products which will not harm the people that eat them (consumers). You can find out more about food safety and the law on page 206. Manufacturers have no legal responsibility to make products suitable for healthy eating; whether a product is healthy or not will depend on its place in the consumer's overall diet. One packet of crisps in an otherwise low-fat diet will do no harm. It is ultimately up to the consumer to choose what to eat.

Glossary

additives : substances added to food materials to enhance flavour, appearance and shelf life

amino acids : the substances from which proteins are made

attribute profile : visual representation of a sensory analysis

basal metabolic rate (BMR) : the energy requirements of a body at complete rest

blast chilling : the rapid chilling of food materials by using blasts of chilled air

blast freezing : the rapid freezing of food materials by using blasts of cold air

brown flour : flour which has had some of the removed bran returned to it

CAD : computer aided design

calorific value : the energy content of food

caramelization : the reaction in which sugar molecules react together to form more complex substances darker in colour with a slightly "burnt" taste

cellulose : the polymer making up the main structure of plants formed by the polymerisation of glucose molecules

clients : those people in business and industry who commission the development of new or improved products

closed loop systems : systems in which information is passed back along the system so controlling the behaviour of the system

COMA (Committee on Medical Aspects of Food Policy) Report : nutritional labelling recommendations

condensation polymerisation : the forming of long chain molecules (polymers) from small molecules (monomers) in which a water molecule if formed for every monomer molecule that joins a chain molecule; the formation of starch from glucose is an example of condensation polymerisation

consumers : those who buy and use a product

dental caries : tooth decay

dietary fibre : non starch polysaccharides such as cellulose in the human diet, they are not digested themselves but help the passage a waste material through the large intestine

dispensible amino acids : amino acid that can be made by the body

emulsifying agent : a substance that helps two immiscible liquids form an emulsion

emulsion : a liquid in liquid colloid in which two usually immiscible liquids are held in a mixture e.g. mayonnaise an oil and vinegar emulsion.

enzymes : substances that catalyse the chemical reactions that occur in living organisms

fatty acids : substances whose molecules are composed of a long hydrocarbon chain (the "fatty" part) and an acid grouping; they combine with glycerol to form fats

foam : a gas liquid or gas solid colloid; e.g. whisked egg whites and meringue

Food Hygiene (amendment) Regulations 1990 and 1991 : legal requirements relating to the preparation and sale of food

Food Hygiene (General) Regulations 1970 : legal requirements relating to the preparation and sale of food

Food Safety Act, 1990 : legal requirements relating to the sale of food for human consumption

food spoilage bacteria : bacteria which cause food to rot

food technology : the name given to the designing and making of food products

gel : a colloid in which a liquid is trapped in a solid

gelatinisation : the setting of a liquid by means of starch

glycerol : the substance that combines with fatty acids to form fats

hard wheat : a wheat which gives regular sized pieces of endosperm when milled

hazard : any feature of a situation which may cause harm or damage

hedonic ranking test : a means of evaluation in which food products are put in an order of preference

human interface : part of a system in which a user interacts with another human e.g. a customer and a sales assistant

image board : a collection of pictures of things people might like, places they might go, activities they might carry out

Improvement Notices : a listing of the improvements required by law in a place where food is handled

indispensible amino acids : amino acids that cannot be made by the body so have to be part of the diet

inputs : the energy, information or materials entering a system are called inputs

interviewing : talking to people in order to obtain their views and opinions

lines of interest : a group of products of a particular type

machine interface : part of a system in which a user interacts with a machine e.g. a customer and an automatic banking machine

mouthfeel : the texture of a food material in the mouth

objective measurements : measurements in which the data obtained is not dependant on the person taking the measurements

operator interfaces : part of a system that is used by the people who run or control the system

outputs : the energy, information or materials leaving a system are called outputs

performance specification : a description of what the product you design will have to do, look like and any other requirements it should meet

polysaccharides : substances whose molecules are made from many sugar molecules joined together

poly unsaturated fatty acids : fatty acids whose molecules are not completely saturated with hydrogen atoms

Prohibition Order : a legal notice preventing the sale or manufacture of food products

rank order : the results of an evaluation test in which food products are put in an order according to a particular quality e.g. in order of increasing sweetness

respiration : the reaction between food and oxygen to produce energy

reviewing : checking design ideas against the brief and specification

risk : the chance of a hazard causing harm or damage

risk assessment : calculating how big a risk is by thinking about whether the harm or damage is likely to happen

risk control : action taken to ensure that the harm or damage is less likely to happen

saturated fatty acids : fatty acids whose molecules are completely saturated with hydrogen atoms

soft wheat : a wheat which gives irregular sized pieces of endosperm when milled

stabilisers : substances added to food to maintain emulsions

strong wheat : wheat with a high protein content

subjective measurements : measurements in which the data obtained is dependant on the person taking the measurements

transit time : rate at which food passes through the body from mouth to anus

triangle test : an evaluation technique in which two identical products are compared with a third

user interfaces : parts of a system used by people

user trip : an evaluation technique in which the food product is tried out

weak wheat : wheat with a low protein content

white flour : flour without bran or germ

wholemeal flour : flour that contains all the wheat

Index

A

acidity **12, 148**
additives **87, 208–9**
advertising, soft drinks **78**
Aero Designs Ltd **35**
aerospace industry **34–5**
aircraft, manufacturing **34–5**
alkalinity **12**
amino acids **134**
Amsterdam, trams **38**
analysis, attributes **80–81**
annotated sketches **9, 82**
anorexia **149**
anti-caking agents **209**
antioxidants **209**
appearance *see* presentation
appropriateness **10, 97**
architects **24–27**
art, design and technology **14**
artificial sweeteners **209**
attribute analysis **80–81**
attribute profile **95**
    taste **102, 103**

B

babies, weaning food **114**
bacteria, contamination **202–4**
Baird, John Logie **30**
bakery, design guide **125–7**
balloons, aerial **34**
bar charts, product presentation **103**
basal metabolic rate (BMR) **145**
batch production **108**
    systems approach **188**
BBC, case study **29–31**
Bell, Sir Alexander Graham **29**
blanching **199**
blast-chilling **191, 195**
blast-freezing **195, 199**
blob score **11**
BMI *see* body mass index
BMR *see* basal metabolic rate
body mass index (BMI) **118**
books, availability **28**
brainstorming, design ideas **77–8**
brand names **58–9, 105**

bread **125**
    production **55–7, 60–2**
    weight measurement **62**
brown flour, bread production **60–2**
browning **135**
building design **24–7**
bulimia **149**
bulk production **47–8**
buses, case study **36–7, 39**
business, information **29**

C

CAD *see* computer aided design
calorific value **88**
Compylobacter jejuni **202**
capability tasks **2**
    assessment **16–17**
    designing and making **6–7, 16–17**
    flow charts **91**
    strategies chooser chart **98**
capping **198**
caramelization **135**
carbohydrates, composition **132**
carbon dioxide **61**, use **200**
caries **150**
case studies **2, 25–69**
    focused **43–69**
    general **24–42**
    interpretation **19**
    types **5**
    writing your own **18**
cassava **56–7**
catering **186–91**
CD ROM, information **31**
Chap books **28**
CHD *see* coronary heart disease
chemical tests **138–40**
chemistry of food **132–40**
children, deficient diet **53**
cholesterol, heart disease **147**
chooser charts
    cooking methods **183–4**

chooser charts (cont)
    finishing methods **185**
    food combining **182**
    food preparation **181**
    nutrition **152–5**
    prototype production **181–5**
clients **99**
closed-loop systems **89**
Clostridium botulinum **202**
Clostridium perfringens **202**
coagulation **135**
coffee shops, design guide **127**
colloids **86–7**
colour **209**
    design **162–5**
    food **163**
    surface **172**
colouring, frozen vegetables **199**
COMA Report **208**
combining food, chooser charts **182**
Committee on Medical Aspects of
    Food Policy *see* COMA Report
communication
    design proposals **99–110**
    mass **29–31**
computer aided design (CAD) **35**
computers
    cost calculation **84**
    nutritional information **84**
    product design **84–5**
condensation polymerization **132**
confectionery **58–9, 74, 128–30**
consumer groups, change **78**
consumers **99**
contamination prevention **203–4**
continuous production **109**
cooking methods
    affect on colour **164**
    affect on nutrition **157**
    affect on smell or flavour **159**
    affect on texture **167**
    chooser chart **183–4**
    contamination prevention **204**
cooling food **195**
copper **52**, diet **54**
cornflakes, case study **49–51**
coronary heart disease (CHD) **147**